DATE DUE

MAR 1 1990	

GAYLORD

D1161172

AN INTRODUCTION TO THE
MATHEMATICS OF LIFE INSURANCE

AN INTRODUCTION TO THE
MATHEMATICS OF LIFE INSURANCE

By

WALTER O. MENGE, Ph.D.

ASSISTANT PROFESSOR OF MATHEMATICS
UNIVERSITY OF MICHIGAN
FELLOW OF THE ACTUARIAL SOCIETY OF AMERICA
FELLOW OF THE AMERICAN INSTITUTE OF ACTUARIES

and

JAMES W. GLOVER, Ph.D.

EDWARD OLNEY PROFESSOR OF MATHEMATICS
UNIVERSITY OF MICHIGAN
FELLOW OF THE AMERICAN INSTITUTE OF ACTUARIES

NEW YORK
THE MACMILLAN COMPANY

Printed in the United States of America

Set up and electrotyped. Published April, 1935.
Sixth Printing, 1954

SET UP AND ELECTROTYPED BY T. MOREY & SON
PRINTED IN THE UNITED STATES OF AMERICA

PREFACE

This book is intended primarily as a text for courses in the mathematics of life insurance in colleges and universities. It also should prove of interest to readers, other than college students, who wish to understand the fundamentals of life insurance. For the study of this text no mathematical preparation, other than that usually included in the high school course, is necessary; but elementary courses in college mathematics and the theory of interest will be found very useful, especially if only a short time is to be devoted to its study.

The material included in this work has been obtained from many sources, including practical actuarial work in the application of the principles as well as many years of teaching the subject. The scope of the book is limited to single life contingencies, together with the application of these probabilities in combination with the theory of interest. The notation used, that of standard actuarial publications, allows the student to continue without interruption with the study of more advanced topics after completing the material contained herein.

Certain of the developments in this text are presented in an entirely new way. The treatment of modified systems of reserves, appearing in Chapter V, furnishes new light on this important practical subject. The definition of net premiums of a modified system as entities, instead of composites, simplifies this rather confusing topic. In Chapter VI there is presented a study of the theoretical methods of determining gross premiums, asset shares, and surrender charges. Experience in the teaching of this subject has shown that students usually display keen interest in this topic.

The general scheme of the book is to provide some elasticity in the time required to cover the material. This is accomplished by the inclusion of many applied problems that should be solved by the student when a complete course is desired. For a shorter survey course many problems may be omitted. If a calculating machine is not available to the student, §§ 40–41 may be omitted without destroying the continuity of the course. Three hundred odd exercises are included with answers. The majority of these require little or no numerical work in their solution. The tables, which are appended, while not entirely complete, are more extensive than those usually included in books of this character and afford greater accuracy than most published books of tables.

The authors are indebted to many friends for valuable suggestions and criticisms. In particular, thanks are extended to Professor James A. Nyswander of the University of Michigan who read the entire manuscript, and whose valuable criticism resulted in conspicuous improvements in the original text.

WALTER O. MENGE
JAMES W. GLOVER

ANN ARBOR, MICHIGAN
March, 1935

CONTENTS

CHAPTER I. THE LIFE TABLE

CHAPTER II. ANNUITIES

CHAPTER III. NET PREMIUMS

CHAPTER IV. NET LEVEL RESERVE

CHAPTER V. MODERN RESERVE SYSTEMS

CONTENTS

AN INTRODUCTION TO THE
MATHEMATICS OF LIFE INSURANCE

CHAPTER I

THE LIFE TABLE

1. Introduction. No prediction can be made with confidence in regard to the time of death of an individual. Although it may be true, as Benjamin Franklin once said, that nothing is certain except death and taxes, it is equally true for the individual life that nothing is so uncertain as the time of death.

It may be known that, out of a large group of persons chosen at random, some will die within a given period of time, but it is not known which particular ones will die. It is this uncertainty, inherent in human life, which gives rise to the necessity for some form of protection against the losses resulting from death. The relative number of deaths from a large group of persons can be predicted with sufficient accuracy to warrant life insurance companies in furnishing insurance protection to persons who satisfy certain requirements in regard to health. Changes in vitality and longevity of the general population progress very slowly, and it is possible, by a careful observation of past experience, to estimate quite closely the number of persons out of a given large group that will die in a year.

The structure of life insurance depends fundamentally upon three elements: (a) the probability of the death of a given individual in a given period of time, (b) the interest

1

rate which can be earned on invested funds, and (c) the rate of expense incurred in the sale and maintenance of a life insurance policy. Inasmuch as the subject of probability plays an important role in the study of the mathematical theory of life insurance, consideration will be given in this chapter to some of the basic principles of this subject.

2. Probability, *a priori* Definition. If an event can happen in h ways and fail in f ways, all of which are equally likely, the probability p of the occurrence of the event is

$$(1) \qquad p = \frac{h}{h+f}$$

and the probability of the failure of the event is

$$(2) \qquad q = \frac{f}{h+f}.$$

This mathematical definition gives a precise meaning to the words *chance* or *probability* as used in regard to the occurrence of an event. Thus, if a bag is known to contain ten balls, seven of which are white, and the other three black, the probability that a ball drawn at random will be white is 7/10. In this problem the number h of the equally likely ways of drawing a white ball is seven, while the number f of equally likely ways in which one can fail to obtain a white ball is three. It should be noted that the denominators of expressions (1) and (2) are the total number of equally likely ways in which the event can either happen or fail.

From definitions (1) and (2), it is obvious that p and q are both less than or equal to unity, while their sum is

$$p + q = \frac{h+f}{h+f} = 1.$$

Thus, the probability of the occurrence of an event plus the probability of the failure of the event is equal to unity. Furthermore, when $f = 0$, $p = 1$, and hence, if an event is certain to occur, the probability of its occurrence is unity.

3. Empirical Probability. There are many important classes of events in which it is impossible to enumerate all of the equally likely ways in which an event can happen or fail. In life insurance, statistics, and in many other fields, the *a priori* definition is impractical and cannot be applied conveniently, and recourse must be made to the method of determining an approximation to the probability by means of observations. In such cases it is necessary that the probability be determined empirically by an observation of the proportion of cases in which the event happens on a large number of occasions. Thus, if it be observed that an event has happened m times in n possible cases (n, a large number) then, in the absence of further information, it may be assumed that m/n is the best estimate of the probability of the event, and that confidence in the reliability of this estimate increases as n increases.

For example, if it be determined that out of 100,000 men alive at exact age 20, the number who died in the following year was 781, an approximation to the probability that a man aged 20 will die in the following year is 0.00781.

A precise formulation of the definition of probability from this empirical point of view would require the limit of the ratio m/n as the number n is increased without bound. It is necessary to assume the existence of such a limit in making precise statements in the theory of probability. Assuming that the limit does exist, it is possible to define the probability of the occurrence of an event as

$$(3) \qquad p = \lim_{n \to \infty} \frac{m}{n}.$$

In statistical applications the limit m/n cannot, in general, be determined, but it is possible to find approximations to the limit which are satisfactory for many practical purposes.

It should be noted that the value of the probability from the empirical point of view is determined by past experience and its use for prediction of future events involves the assumption that the experience of the future will duplicate that of the past. This expectation, of course, will not always be fulfilled, but where large numbers are involved, slight variations will have little significance, and in any case, the assumption is the best and most convenient one available.

It is important to recognize that the statement "the probability of an event is 2/3" means (a) if a large number of trials are taken it is expected that approximately 2/3 of them will be successful, and (b) that as the number of trials is increased, the ratio of successes to trials will approach the limit 2/3. This statement does not mean that in a given number of trials, say 60, exactly 2/3 of them, or 40, will be successful, but rather that the number 40 represents the best prediction of the number of successful trials. It may happen that more or less than this expected number will occur.

4. Theorems on Probability. Two or more events are said to be *mutually exclusive* if the occurrence of any one of them excludes the occurrence of any of the others. Two events are said to be *dependent* or *independent* according as the occurrence of either one of them does or does not affect the probability of the occurrence of the other.

THEOREM I. *The probability of the occurrence of any one of a number of mutually exclusive events is the sum of the respective probabilities of the individual events.*

Let the probabilities $p_1, p_2, \cdots, p_r$ of r mutually exclusive events be (after reducing to a common denominator)

$$\frac{h_1}{n}, \frac{h_2}{n}, \cdots, \frac{h_r}{n},$$

respectively. Then any one of these events can happen in

$$h_1 + h_2 + \cdots + h_r$$

equally likely ways, and the probability of the **occurrence of** any one of the events is

$$\frac{h_1 + h_2 + \cdots + h_r}{n} = p_1 + p_2 + \cdots + p_r.$$

THEOREM II. *The probability of the occurrence of all of a set of independent events is the product of the respective probabilities of the individual events.*

Let the probabilities of two independent events be $p_1 = h_1/n_1$ and $p_2 = h_2/n_2$, respectively, where h_1 and h_2 represent respectively the number of equally likely ways in which the events can happen. For each way in which the first event can happen there are h_2 ways in which the second can also happen, so that both events can succeed in $h_1 \cdot h_2$ equally likely ways. In a similar way, the total number of ways in which the two events can happen or fail is $n_1 \cdot n_2$, and hence from the definition the probability of the occurrence of both events is

$$\frac{h_1 \cdot h_2}{n_1 \cdot n_2} = p_1 p_2.$$

The extension of this proof to more than two events is left to the student.

THEOREM III. *If the probability of a first event is p_1, and if, after this has happened, the probability of a second event is p_2, the probability that both events will happen in the specified order is $p_1 \cdot p_2$.*

The proof of this theorem is entirely analogous to that of the previous theorem. The extension of Theorem III to any number of events is obvious.

EXERCISES—LIST I

1. If the probabilities that A and B survive a certain period are 0.7 and 0.8 respectively, what is the probability
  (a) that both A and B survive,
  (b) that at least one dies?

SOLUTION. (a) Assuming that the deaths of A and B are independent events, the desired probability is, by Theorem II,

$$0.7 \times 0.8 = 0.56.$$

(b) Events (a) and (b) are mutually exclusive events, one of which is certain to happen. Hence, the probability of the occurrence of one or the other of these events is unity. Employing Theorem I, we find for the probability of event (b)

$$1 - 0.56 = 0.44.$$

2. A bag contains 5 white, 3 red, and 4 black balls. If a ball is drawn at random, what is the probability that it is a red ball? A white ball? A white or red ball?

3. If two dice are thrown, what is the probability of two threes? Two fours? A three paired with a four?

4. The probability of an individual aged 30 living 10 years is 0.9 and the probability of an individual aged 40 living 10 years is 0.8. What is the probability that an individual aged 30

(a) lives to reach age 50,

(b) dies between ages 40 and 50,

(c) dies before reaching age 40?

5. Two cards are drawn at random without replacement from a deck of 52. What is the probability that both the cards drawn are aces? Both kings? An ace followed by a king? A king followed by an ace? An ace and a king drawn in either order?

6. What is the probability of a particular baseball team winning all three of a series of games, assuming the teams are evenly matched? Winning two and losing one in any order?

7. Three cards are drawn without replacement from a deck of 52. What is the probability that all the cards are aces? Two aces followed by a king? An ace, king, and queen drawn in any order?

8. Answer questions (5) and (7) under the assumption that the cards are replaced after each drawing.

9. A traveler has four connections to make in order that he may reach his destination on time. If the probability of making each connection is 3/4, what is the probability of his making all of the connections?

10. The probability of team A winning a game from team B is 3/5. What is the probability that A will win two or more out of a series of three?

11. If the probabilities of A, B, C, and D surviving a certain period are 3/4, 4/5, 5/6, and 6/7, respectively, what is the probability that
  (a) all four will survive the period,
  (b) all four will die in the period,
  (c) at least one dies in the period,
  (d) at least one survives the period?

12. Two dice are thrown and the sum of the upper faces computed. What is the probability of throwing a seven? A two? An eleven? Any number greater than eight?

13. If a bag contains 4 red and 3 white balls, and a second bag contains 2 red and 5 white balls, what is the probability of drawing one red and one white ball in two drawings, one from each bag?

14. What is the probability of throwing n heads in n throws of a coin? One tail and the rest heads?

15. If the probability that the age of a man, selected at random from a group of men, is between 20 and 35 years is 2/3, and the probability that it is between 20 and 25 is 1/4, what is the probability that his age is between 25 and 35?

16. If the probabilities of surviving ten years are 0.8, 0.7, and 0.6 for persons of ages 30, 40, and 50, respectively, what is the probability that an individual now age 30 will die between ages 50 and 60?

5. Selection. A *select* group is one which has not been chosen at random. The *selection* of such a group may be deliberate, as in the case of a life insurance company requiring a satisfactory medical examination prior to insurance. A group chosen in this manner may be expected to live longer on the average than a group chosen at random. The selection of a group may be automatic as in the case of emigration from one country to another, where it may be expected that only persons in reasonably good health will migrate. Individuals purchasing life annuities, payable only during the life of the individual, from insurance companies form a select group, inasmuch as an individual in poor health usually will not buy such an annuity.

It has been observed that the effect of these types of selection upon the mortality rate of the select group diminishes with the lapse of time from the date of selection, and usually entirely disappears in a period of five or ten years. Thus, two groups of persons, one formed from the survivors of those who insured fifteen years ago at age 30, and the other from the survivors of those who insured ten years ago at age 35 (all the members of the two groups being, therefore, now of the same age), would probably show about the same mortality rate.

One of the important problems of the actuary lies in the choice of the proper mortality table, that is, the mortality table which seems to best fit the group of lives considered.

6. Sources of Mortality Tables. The basis of the theory of life insurance is the mortality or life table. A mortality table has been defined as "the instrument by means of which are measured the probabilities of life and death." A mortality table is purely a record of past experience and naturally its use in predicting future events implies the expectation that the experience of the past will be duplicated in the future. In the construction of a mortality table, the investigations which are undertaken are designed to yield at each age the *rate of mortality*, that is, the probability that a life of a given age will die within a year. The two principal sources of life tables are general population statistics obtained from the census and the mortality records of life insurance companies.

Many important mortality tables have been based upon the experience of the general population. The numbers of deaths are obtained at each age from the official records of deaths, and the rate of mortality at any age is obtained by dividing the number of deaths by an adjusted figure representing the number exposed to the risk of death at that age. Such a table is unsuitable for use by a life insurance company. Insured lives form a "select" group, from which those lives subject to high rates of mortality have been eliminated by medical examination or otherwise. The population table, however, includes many in poor health, and others engaged in hazardous or unhealthy occupations. It is to be expected, therefore, that the rates of mortality in a table constructed from population records will be higher than the rates of mortality in a table based on the experience of life insurance companies.

The rates of mortality among the general population in certain parts of this country are shown in the United States Life Tables.* These tables are based on the census statistics of the original registration area only, which lies principally in the northeastern part of this country. Figures were not available for all states, so that a table on the basis of the entire country could not be constructed. Different sections of the country exhibit decidedly different rates of mortality. In some of the southern and southwestern states, such as Alabama, Mississippi, and Arkansas, the rate of mortality is much greater than it is in the northern states. A table based upon the country as a whole, even if it were available, would be inapplicable for many purposes, and might be misleading.

The United States Life Tables contain separate tabulations by states, and each is further subdivided to show the rates of mortality in respect to white and colored persons, male and female lives, native-born and foreign-born, and among those residing in urban and rural districts. Generally speaking, the rate of mortality is lower among white persons than among colored, the rates for colored persons being almost double that for the white persons for the greater part of the table. The rate of mortality is lower among females than among males, and the foreign-born rate is lower from ages twenty to forty than it is among native-born, but this is probably because these are the ages at which most of the immigration takes place. The superiority of native-born

* *United States Life Tables*, 1890, 1901, 1910, and 1901–1910, J. W. Glover, published by Bureau of the Census, Washington, D. C.

persons shows itself after the effects of the selection due to immigration have disappeared. The mortality rate is lower in rural districts than in cities, although this may be partly due to a greater overstatement of ages among older persons in rural districts.

There are in existence many life tables formed from the experience of one or more life insurance companies. In the construction of such a table the number of deaths at each age is recorded and compared with the number of lives exposed to the risk of death at that age. The quotient of these two figures gives the rate of mortality. It is to be expected that, regardless of the source from which the statistics are obtained, the empirical data will not yield a smooth sequence of rates from age to age, and some process of "graduation" is necessary to smooth out the irregularities.

The American Experience Table is undoubtedly the most widely known mortality table in this country. It was constructed about 1860 in the manner described above presumably from the experience of the Mutual Life Insurance Company of New York, and, although it no longer accurately measures the mortality rate, it is at present the basis for many of the calculations of life insurance actuaries in this country. This table is an "ultimate table," inasmuch as it shows the rate of mortality after the effect of the selection caused by the medical examination has disappeared.

In 1915, the larger life insurance organizations of the United States cooperated in gathering experience for the American Men Mortality Table.* This experience was taken from the records of insured lives for the period of 1900–1915 inclusive, and shows not only the "ultimate" rate of mortality

* See *American-Canadian Mortality Investigation* (3 volumes), published by the Actuarial Society of America, New York City.

for the period after the effect of the medical selection has disappeared (assumed to be five years), but also shows the adjusted rates of mortality, called "select" rates, for each of the years of the five year period during which the medical examination and other selection methods are effective. The following extract from this table shows the mortality rates for selected ages.

AMERICAN MEN MORTALITY TABLE

RATE OF MORTALITY PER 1000

Age at Issue	Year of Insurance						At-tained Age
	1	2	3	4	5	6 and Over	
15	2.47	3.24	3.41	3.55	3.72	3.92	20
16	2.52	3.31	3.48	3.63	3.82	4.02	21
17	2.56	3.37	3.55	3.73	3.92	4.12	22
18	2.61	3.44	3.64	3.81	4.00	4.18	23
19	2.66	3.52	3.72	3.89	4.07	4.25	24
20	2.73	3.59	3.80	3.96	4.13	4.31	25
21	2.78	3.66	3.86	4.01	4.18	4.35	26
22	2.83	3.72	3.91	4.06	4.21	4.39	27
23	2.86	3.76	3.96	4.08	4.24	4.41	28
24	2.91	3.80	3.99	4.11	4.26	4.43	29
25	2.93	3.84	4.02	4.12	4.27	4.46	30
26	2.95	3.86	4.04	4.13	4.28	4.48	31
27	2.98	3.88	4.06	4.14	4.29	4.51	32
28	2.98	3.91	4.06	4.14	4.32	4.59	33
29	2.99	3.92	4.08	4.17	4.37	4.68	34

etc.

In the preceding table the figure 3.91 given for the third year of insurance at age 22 indicates that 0.00391 is the probability that an individual now aged 24 (who was accepted for life insurance two years ago at age 22) will die before attaining age 25.

Other recent tables constructed from the records of life insurance companies are the American Annuitants Select Table * and the Combined Annuitants Table.†

The following table shows at quinquennial ages the rates of mortality per 1000 according to several of the well-known mortality tables compiled from population and insured life experience.

RATE OF MORTALITY PER 1000

Age	American Experience	American [a] Men Ultimate	U.S. Life Table 1910	American Annuitants [a] Male	American Annuitants [a] Female
15	7.63	—	2.84	—	—
20	7.80	3.92	4.68	—	—
25	8.06	4.31	5.54	4.31	4.01
30	8.43	4.46	6.51	4.99	4.52
35	8.95	4.78	8.04	6.00	5.27
40	9.79	5.84	9.39	7.51	6.39
45	11.16	7.94	11.52	9.78	8.07
50	13.78	11.58	14.37	13.15	10.56
55	18.57	17.47	20.03	18.17	14.28
60	26.69	26.68	28.58	25.66	19.84
65	40.13	40.66	41.06	36.73	28.09
70	61.99	61.47	59.52	53.05	40.31
75	94.37	91.94	87.37	76.98	58.27
80	144.47	135.74	130.28	111.65	84.58
85	235.55	197.07	183.80	161.12	122.51
90	454.54	280.35	249.62	230.04	176.46
95	1000.00	387.76	325.02	323.06	250.84
100	—	562.50	401.91	456.79	349.79
105	—	—	500.22	1000.00	772.73

[a] Table shows mortality rate after the "select" period of five years.

EXERCISES—LIST II

Fill in the numerical values from the American Men Mortality Table (page 11) for each of the following problems, but do not multiply.

1. What is the probability that a man now aged 21, who was accepted for insurance a year ago, will live to reach age 23?

* See Transactions of the Actuarial Society of America, vol. 28, p. 363.
† See Transactions of the Actuarial Society of America, vol. 31, p. 62.

SOLUTION. The probability of such an individual, age 21, dying within one year is 0.00359 according to the table. Hence, the probability of living one year is $1 - 0.00359 = 0.99641$. The probability of an individual age 22, accepted for life insurance two years ago, living a year is $1 - 0.00380 = 0.99620$. Hence, by Theorem II, the desired probability is $(0.99641)(0.99620)$.

2. What is the probability that a man, now being accepted for life insurance at age 26, will live to reach age 30?

3. What is the probability that an individual now aged 20, who was accepted for insurance two years ago, will die between ages 21 and 22?

4. What is the probability that an individual, now aged 17, who was accepted for insurance at age 15, will live to reach age 25?

5. What is the probability that an individual, now being accepted for insurance at age 20, will die before reaching age 25?

7. The Mortality Table. It is convenient to represent the phrase "a life aged x" by the notation (x). The symbol q_x is used to designate the rate of mortality at age x, that is, the probability that (x) will die between ages x and $x + 1$. If p_x denotes the probability that (x) will live to age $x + 1$, it follows that

$$p_x + q_x = 1$$

for all ages.

Let l_x represent the number of persons who, according to the mortality table, attain precise age x in any year of time. The symbol d_x denotes the number who, out of the l_x lives attaining age x, die before attaining age $x + 1$. Hence, one has immediately

(4) $$d_x = l_x \cdot q_x,$$

and

(5) $$l_{x+1} = l_x - d_x.$$

In the previous section methods of obtaining the numerical values of the rate of mortality q_x were described. After these rates have been determined for every age, it is possible to start with an arbitrary number of births l_0 (called the *radix* of the table), and, by means of equations (4) and (5), to construct columns of l_x and d_x. It is not essential that the table start at birth; it may begin with any arbitrary radix, l_a, at any convenient age a. Thus, the American Experience Table (see Table II of the Appendix) begins with a radix of 100,000 at age 10 and

$d_{10} = 749 = l_{10}\, q_{10}$, where $l_{10} = 100,000$ and $q_{10} = 0.007490$,

$l_{11} = 99,251 = l_{10} - d_{10}$,

$d_{11} = 746 = l_{11} \cdot q_{11}$, where $l_{11} = 99,251$ and $q_{11} = 0.007516$,

$l_{12} = 98,505 = l_{11} - d_{11}$,

and so on.

The symbol ω is used to denote the final or *limiting* age of the table, beyond which it is practical to assume that all entries in the l_x column approximate zero. In the American Experience Table the limiting age is 95, since values of l_x beyond this age are so small that they do not affect subsequent calculations.

It should be noted that no figure in either the l_x column or in the d_x column has any meaning in itself. Each value of l_x represents the expected number of survivors who reach age x this year from the l_{x-1} lives who reached age $x - 1$ in the previous year, or from the l_{x-2} lives who reached age $x - 2$ in the second previous year, and so on.

EXERCISES—LIST III

1. Prove by means of equations (4) and (5) the following identities:

    (a) $l_x = d_x + d_{x+1} + \cdots + d_\omega.$

    (b) $l_x - l_{x+n} = d_x + d_{x+1} + \cdots + d_{x+n-1}.$

    (c) $l_{x+n} = l_x \cdot p_x \cdot p_{x+1} \cdots p_{x+n-1}.$

2. Given that $l_{15} = 100,000$; and the rates of mortality at ages 15, 16, 17, 18, and 19 are 0.0050, 0.0054, 0.0058, 0.0062, and 0.0070, respectively, compute columns of l_x, d_x, and p_x for these ages.

3. Verify equations (4) and (5) for the American Experience Table for ages 40 to 45, inclusive.

4. Check numerically the identities given in Exercise 1 for the American Experience Table, using $x = 90$ and $n = 3$.

8. Notation. The symbol $_np_x$ means the probability that (x) will live to reach age $x + n$. Out of the l_x persons alive at age x there are l_{x+n} survivors at age $x + n$; consequently

$$_np_x = \frac{l_{x+n}}{l_x}.$$

The probability that (x) will die before reaching age $x + n$ is denoted by $|_nQ_x$. Hence

$$|_nQ_x = \frac{d_x + d_{x+1} + \cdots + d_{x+n-1}}{l_x} = \frac{l_x - l_{x+n}}{l_x}.$$

The symbol $_m|q_x$ is used to denote the probability that a person now aged x will die in the year following the attainment of age $x + m$, or between ages $x + m$ and $x + m + 1$. Since, according to the mortality table, d_{x+m} individuals will die in this age interval out of l_x alive at age x, it follows that

$$_m|q_x = \frac{d_{x+m}}{l_x}.$$

The probability that (x) will die in the n year period following the attainment of age $x + m$, or in the period of time between age $x + m$ and age $x + m + n$, is denoted by the symbol $_m|_nQ_x$. It follows immediately that

$$_m|_nQ_x = \frac{d_{x+m} + d_{x+m+1} + \cdots + d_{x+m+n-1}}{l_x},$$

or

$$(6) \qquad _m|_nQ_x = \frac{l_{x+m} - l_{x+m+n}}{l_x}.$$

In considering the foregoing notation it should be noted that the letter "p" with proper subscripts is used to denote the probability of an individual living a given period; whereas, the letter "q" is used to denote the probability of an individual dying during a given period, and furthermore, the capital "Q" is used whenever the period in which the death may occur is greater than one year. The notation $_{m|n}Q_x$ is entirely general and may be specialized to yield the following results:

$$q_x = {_{0|1}Q_x}, \qquad _{|n}Q_x = {_{0|n}Q_x}, \qquad _{m|}q_x = {_{m|1}Q_x}.$$

EXERCISES—LIST IV

1. From the American Experience Table find the numerical values of the following probabilities (give the proper symbol in each case):

(a) that a man aged 20 will live at least 25 years more,

(b) that a man aged 30 will die in the year following the attainment of age 45,

(c) that a man aged 35 will die between ages 60 and 70,

(d) that a man aged 40 will live to age 55 but not to age 60,

(e) that a man aged 45 will die within five years,

(f) that a man aged 20 will die between ages 45 and 50.

(g) Explain why the answer to (f) is the product of the answers to parts (a) and (e).

2. State in words the probabilities represented by the following symbols:

$$_{10}p_{21}; \qquad p_{21}; \qquad _{10|}q_{30}; \qquad _{10|2}Q_{30}; \qquad q_{40}; \qquad _{15|5}Q_{50}.$$

3. The probability $_{n}p_x$ may be considered as the probability of the compound event consisting of (x) living one year, $(x+1)$ living one year, $(x+2)$ living one year . . ., and $(x+n-1)$ living one year. From Theorem II the probability of this compound event is

$$p_x \; p_{x+1} \; p_{x+2} \cdots \; p_{x+n-1}.$$

Show algebraically that this expression is equal to $_{n}p_x$.

4. Prove the following identities:

(a) $\qquad\qquad _{m+1}p_x + {_{m|}q_x} = {_{m}p_x},$

(b) $\qquad\qquad _{m+n}p_x + {_{m|n}Q_x} = {_{m}p_x},$

(c) $\qquad _{m+n}p_x = {_{m}p_x} \cdot {_{n}p_{x+m}} = {_{n}p_x} \cdot {_{m}p_{x+n}}.$

5. The probability that a man aged 30 and another man aged 50 will both survive a period of twenty years is 0.4. Out of 48,000 men alive at age 30, 3000 will die before they attain age 40. Calculate the probability that a man now aged 40 will die within the next 30 years.

6. Prove the following identities:

(a) $\qquad\qquad _{m|}q_x = {_{m}p_x} \cdot q_{x+m},$

(b) $\qquad\qquad _{m|n}Q_x = {_{m}p_x} \cdot {_{|n}Q_{x+m}}.$

9. Expectation of Life. By the *expectation of life* is meant the average number of years to be lived in the future by persons now aged x. If we assume that all the deaths that occur in any year take place at the very beginning of that year, out of an original group of l_x persons at age x there will be l_{x+1} persons who survive to the end of the first year, and there will be a total of l_{x+1} years lived by the whole group during the first year following age x. Similarly, the group will live a total of l_{x+2} additional years during the second year following age x, l_{x+3} additional years during the third year, and so on. Adding these whole years together and dividing by the number of persons, l_x, in the original group, we find the average number of years to be lived in the future by individuals now aged x,

$$(7) \qquad e_x = \frac{l_{x+1} + l_{x+2} + l_{x+3} + \cdots + l_\omega}{l_x}.$$

This fraction is called the *curtate expectation* since it neglects the fractional parts of years lived by those who die in any year.

Under the assumption that the deaths during any year of age are distributed uniformly throughout the year, so that on the average each person will live half a year in the year of his death, the *complete expectation* of life at age x is found by adding $1/2$ to the curtate expectation. Hence,

$$(8) \qquad \overset{\circ}{e}_x = e_x + \frac{1}{2} = \frac{1}{2} + \frac{l_{x+1} + l_{x+2} + \cdots + l_\omega}{l_x},$$

approximately.

The expectation of life is often useful in making a rough analysis of problems which would otherwise have to be solved by more elaborate means to be considered later. It is often supposed, however, by those unacquainted with actuarial methods that the expectation of life is fundamental in actuarial calculations. That this is not the case will be seen from the developments of the succeeding chapters.

EXERCISES—LIST V

1. Check the values of the expectation of life given in the American Experience Table for ages 75, 85, and 90.

2. Assuming that deaths are uniformly distributed throughout the year, show that

$$\overset{\circ}{e}_x = \tfrac{1}{2}(q_x + 3 \cdot {}_1|q_x + 5 \cdot {}_2|q_x + 7 \cdot {}_3|q_x + \cdots).$$

3. Prove $\qquad e_x = p_x + {}_2p_x + {}_3p_x + \cdots.$

4. (a) Show that $\quad e_x = p_x(1 + e_{x+1}).$
(b) Prove

$$\frac{e_x \cdot e_{x+1} \cdot e_{x+2} \cdots e_{x+n-1}}{(1 + e_{x+1})(1 + e_{x+2})(1 + e_{x+3}) \cdots (1 + e_{x+n})} = {}_np_x.$$

5. Show that $\quad 1 + e_x = q_x + p_x(1 + q_{x+1}) + {}_2p_x(1 + q_{x+2}) + \cdots.$

REVIEW EXERCISE—LIST VI

1. Given the following table of mortality, deduce columns for d_x, q_x, p_x, e_x, and $\overset{\circ}{e}_x$.

x	90	91	92	93	94	95	96
l_x	850	450	210	75	20	4	0

2. If $l_x = k(86 - x)$, where k is a constant, show that

$$d_x = k; \qquad p_x = \frac{85 - x}{86 - x}; \qquad q_x = \frac{1}{86 - x}.$$

3. From the American Men Mortality Table, § 6, find the probability that an individual now being accepted for life insurance, at age 17 will

(a) survive to age 20,

(b) die between ages 18 and 19,

(c) survive to age 19.

4. The probability that at least one of the two lives A and B will die in the next ten years is 0.44. The probability that at least one of the two lives will survive the period is 0.94. Find the probability that A will be living at the end of the ten years.

5. A husband is aged 22 and a wife 24 at the date of their marriage; what is the probability that they will live to celebrate their silver wedding? Their golden wedding? Use the American Experience Table to answer this problem.

6. Using the American Experience Table find numerical answers to the following probabilities:

(a) that (30) will die between ages 65 and 70,

(b) that (50) will survive to age 70,

(c) that (20) will die between ages 80 and 85.

7. Plot a graph showing, at age intervals of five years, the values of q_x as given by the American Experience Table.

8. Between what two consecutive ages, according to the American Experience Table, is a man now aged 35 most likely to die? What is the probability that he will die in that year?

CHAPTER II

ANNUITIES

10. Compound Interest. The mathematical theory of life insurance involves the assumption that money is constantly productive. Life insurance probably constitutes the best example of long-time finance, or investment extended over a considerable period of time, and thus it is necessary that some consideration be given to the most important principles of interest. Methods of computing interest may be classified generally into two classes: (a) *simple interest*, in which the principal is considered as remaining constant throughout the transaction, and (b) *compound interest*, in which the interest previously earned is periodically "compounded," or added to the principal, thus producing a new principal to be used in the ensuing period. Life insurance companies invariably use compound interest with a period of one year as the time between the successive "compoundings"; our discussion here will be limited to interest calculated upon this basis.

If we denote the annual rate of interest by i, then the interest earned on a principal of P in one year will be $P \cdot i$, and the total accumulated amount, including both principal and interest, will be $P(1 + i)$ by the end of one year. This new principal, $P(1 + i)$, when invested for the second year earns interest of $P(1 + i)i$, and the total accumulated amount at the end of that year will be

$$P(1 + i) + P(1 + i)i = P(1 + i)^2.$$

Similarly, during the third year the principal invested will be $P(1 + i)^2$, the interest earned $P(1 + i)^2 i$, and the total

20

accumulated amount

$$P(1 + i)^2 + P(1 + i)^2 i = P(1 + i)^3.$$

In general, after n years have elapsed, the total accumulated amount A, including the original principal of P and the interest earned in the meantime, is

(9) $$A = P(1 + i)^n.$$

Dividing this equation by $(1 + i)^n$, we obtain

(10) $$P = A(1 + i)^{-n} = A \cdot v^n,$$

where $v = (1 + i)^{-1}$.

The principal P is called the *present value* or *discounted value* of A. It may be considered as the sum which placed at compound interest at the rate i will amount or accumulate to A by the end of the n years.

Tables of the functions $(1 + i)^n$ and v^n at $3\frac{1}{2}\%$ interest are given in Table I in the Appendix.

11. Annuity Certain. An *annuity certain* is a sequence of periodic payments, usually of equal size, payable over a fixed term of years, it being assumed that each payment is sure to be made at the time when it is due. The time between successive payments is called the *payment interval*. We shall restrict the present discussion to annuities with a payment interval of one year. It is convenient to consider that each annuity payment pertains to some payment interval, either immediately preceding or immediately following the payment. The time from the beginning of the first payment interval to the end of the last payment interval is called the *term* of the annuity. The *annual rent* of an annuity is the sum of the payments which occur in any one year, and since only annuities with annual payments are under consideration, the annual rent will be the annuity payment. An annuity whose payments are made at the beginning of each payment interval is called an annuity *due*, whereas the term annuity *immediate* is applied whenever the payments are made at the end of each payment interval. The *present value* or *single premium* for an annuity is the sum of the present values of the payments taken at the beginning of its term, whereas the *amount* of an annuity is the sum of the accumulated amounts of the payments taken at the end of its term, each payment being accumulated from the date when it was due. Obviously, the present value and the amount of an annuity will depend for their values upon the interest rate to be used. Since the present value and the amount of an annuity represent the values of the same payments taken at different times, the present value is equal to the amount discounted over the term of the annuity.

Consider an annuity with a payment of \$1 paid at the end of the first year, \$1 paid at the end of the second year, and so on until finally \$1 is paid at the end of the nth year. Such a sequence of payments forms, according to the definition, an annuity immediate with annual rent \$1. Let $s_{\overline{n}|}$ denote the sum of the accumulated values of the payments taken at the end of the nth year at the interest rate i, compounded annually. The payment made at the end of the first year will accumulate for $n - 1$ years, the payment made at the end of the second year will accumulate for $n - 2$ years, and so on, the final payment of \$1 earning no interest. Upon successively applying equation (9), one has

$$s_{\overline{n}|} = (1 + i)^{n-1} + (1 + i)^{n-2} + \cdots + (1 + i) + 1.$$

The multiplication of both sides of this equation by $(1 + i)$ yields

$$(1 + i)s_{\overline{n}|} = (1 + i)^n + (1 + i)^{n-1} + \cdots + (1 + i)^2 + (1 + i).$$

Subtracting the first equation from the second, we obtain

$$i \cdot s_{\overline{n}|} = (1 + i)^n - 1,$$

whence it follows that

$$(11) \qquad s_{\overline{n}|} = \frac{(1 + i)^n - 1}{i}.$$

Let $a_{\overline{n}|}$ denote the present value of the same annuity, that is, the discounted value of these payments at the beginning of the first year. To obtain an expression for $a_{\overline{n}|}$, discount the amount $s_{\overline{n}|}$ for n years (the term of the annuity) and obtain

$$a_{\overline{n}|} = (1 + i)^{-n} s_{\overline{n}|} = \frac{(1 + i)^{-n}(1 + i)^n - (1 + i)^{-n}}{i};$$

hence

$$(12) \qquad a_{\overline{n}|} = \frac{1 - v^n}{i}.$$

Tables of the values of $s_{\overline{n}|}$ and $a_{\overline{n}|}$ at $3\frac{1}{2}\%$ interest are found in Table I in the Appendix.

Let us suppose that the payments described above were made at the beginning of each year instead of at the end. Such an annuity would be an annuity *due* and each of its payments would be equivalent to $(1 + i)$ paid at the end of the same year. Hence, if $\$_{\overline{n}|}$ and $a_{\overline{n}|}$ denote respectively the amount and present value of the annuity due, it follows that

$$\$_{\overline{n}|} = (1 + i)s_{\overline{n}|}$$
$$a_{\overline{n}|} = (1 + i)a_{\overline{n}|}.$$

Inserting the value of $s_{\overline{n}|}$ given by equation (11), we obtain

$$\$_{\overline{n}|} = \frac{1 + i}{i}\left[(1 + i)^n - 1\right]$$
$$= \frac{(1 + i)^{n+1} - (1 + i)}{i} = \frac{(1 + i)^{n+1} - 1}{i} - 1.$$

Hence it follows that

$$(13) \qquad \$_{\overline{n}|} = s_{\overline{n+1}|} - 1.$$

Similarly

$$a_{\overline{n}|} = \frac{1+i}{i}\left[1 - v^n\right] = \frac{(1+i) - v^{n-1}}{i}$$

$$= 1 + \frac{1 - v^{n-1}}{i},$$

and hence

$$(14) \qquad a_{\overline{n}|} = 1 + a_{\overline{n-1}|}.$$

Equations (13) and (14) are useful in obtaining the numerical values of $\$_{\overline{n}|}$ and $a_{\overline{n}|}$ from the values of $s_{\overline{n}|}$ and $a_{\overline{n}|}$, respectively, given in Table I.

It should be noted that $a_{\overline{n}|}$ represents the value of a sequence of payments one payment interval before the first payment is due; $a_{\overline{n}|}$ represents the value at the time of the first payment; $s_{\overline{n}|}$ the value at the time of the last payment; and $\$_{\overline{n}|}$ the value one payment interval after the last payment is made.

EXERCISES—LIST VII

Assume an interest rate of $3\frac{1}{2}\%$, compounded annually, in the following problems.

1. A beneficiary under a life insurance policy is offered the option of $10,000 cash or a sequence of equal payments at the end of each year for ten years. Find the annual payment.

SOLUTION. Let R be the amount of each annual payment. Then the present value of the annuity immediate of R per year may be represented by the product

$$R \cdot a_{\overline{10}|}.$$

Since this option is to be equivalent to $10,000 in cash, one immediately writes the equation

$$R \cdot a_{\overline{10}|} = 10,000,$$

whence, using Table I, we find

$$R = \frac{10,000}{a_{\overline{10}|}} = 10,000(0.120241) = \$1202.41.$$

2. Solve Exercise 1 when the payments are to be made at the beginning of each year for ten years. For fifteen years.

3. (a) Find the accumulated amount of $2000 invested for twenty years. Seventy years.

(b) What is the present value of $1000 due at the end of ten years? A hundred years?

4. An individual aged 30 pays $5000 to a life insurance company in exchange for a contract in which the company agrees to pay a fixed sum when the individual reaches age 60. If the individual dies before age 60 the company agrees to return immediately to his heirs the $5000 and accumulated interest to the date of his death. What amount should the individual receive when he attains age 60?

5. If d (called the *rate of discount*) satisfies the equation $d = iv$, show that

(a) $d = 1 - v,$

(b) $s_{\overline{n}|} = \dfrac{(1+i)^n - 1}{d},$

(c) $a_{\overline{n}|} = \dfrac{1 - v^n}{d},$

(d) $s_{\overline{n}|}^{-1} = a_{\overline{n}|}^{-1} - d.$

6. Prove the identities:

(a) $a_{\overline{n+1}|} = a_{\overline{n}|} + v^{n+1},$

(b) $s_{\overline{n+1}|} = s_{\overline{n}|} + (1+i)^n,$

(c) $v^n = v \cdot a_{\overline{n}|} - a_{\overline{n-1}|},$

(d) $v^n = 1 - i \cdot a_{\overline{n}|}.$

12. Pure Endowment. Let us suppose that l_x persons, all of age x, desire by equal contributions at the present time to provide a payment of $1 to each one that survives the succeeding n years. As l_{x+n} survivors will be living at the end of the n year period, a fund of l_{x+n} dollars must be on hand at that time. The present value of this fund is $v^n l_{x+n}$. Since this amount is to be raised at the present time from the l_x persons, the individual contribution, which we shall denote by $_nE_x$, is

$$(15) \qquad _nE_x = \frac{v^n l_{x+n}}{l_x} = v^n \cdot {}_np_x.$$

The benefit described above constitutes for each individual what is known as a *pure endowment*, that is, a payment to be made at the end of a specified number of years only in event that a designated individual (x) survives to receive it. The individual's contribution or *premium*, $_nE_x$, depends for its value upon the rate of interest and the probability that the final payment of \$1 will be received, and may be considered as the present value of the pure endowment. The present value A of an n year pure endowment of R payable to a man now aged x if he survives the n years is

$$A = R \cdot {_nE_x} = R \cdot v^n \cdot {_np_x}.$$

If both the numerator and denominator of the second member of equation (15) are multiplied by v^x, we obtain

$$_nE_x = \frac{v^{x+n}l_{x+n}}{v^x l_x}.$$

Designate by D_x the product $v^x \cdot l_x$ and by D_{x+n} the product $v^{x+n}l_{x+n}$. Thus we write $D_{25} = v^{25}\, l_{25}$, $D_{50} = v^{50}\, l_{50}$, etc.

Inserting these symbols in the previous equation, we have

(16) $$_nE_x = \frac{D_{x+n}}{D_x}.$$

The notation D_x is one of several auxiliary symbols, known as *commutation symbols*, which play an important role in practical calculations. It will be noticed as the theory develops that direct use of the values given in a mortality table is rarely made, except to compute the values of the commutation symbols. Tables of the values of D_x and other commutation symbols upon the basis of the American Experience Table with various rates of interest have been computed and are in common use. Unless otherwise specified, all computations in the numerical problems are to be based upon this table with interest at $3\frac{1}{2}\%$ per annum. Commutation columns at this rate of interest are given in Table III, whereas values of $_nE_x$ and its reciprocal, for selected values of n, are given in Tables VII and VIII, respectively.

EXERCISES—LIST VIII

1. Two payments of $1000 each are to be received at the end of five and ten years, respectively. Find their present value

(a) if they are certain to be received;

(b) if they are to be received only if (45) is alive to receive them.

SOLUTION. (a) Since the payments are assumed to be paid in any event, discount due to the interest factor only need be considered, and we have immediately

$$\text{present value} = 1000(1.035)^{-5} + 1000(1.035)^{-10} = \$1550.89.$$

(Table I)

(b) In this case the payments constitute two pure endowments payable at ages 50 and 55, respectively. Hence, the total present value is

$$1000 \, {}_5E_{45} + 1000 \, {}_{10}E_{45}$$

Employing Table VII to find numerical values for the pure endowment symbols, we have

$$1000(0.7923786) + 1000(0.6170699) = \$1409.45.$$

2. A man now aged 20 is promised a gift of $5000 when he reaches age 35. Find the present value of the promise.

3. Show that

(a) ${}_mE_x \cdot {}_nE_{x+m} = {}_{m+n}E_x$;

(b) ${}_nE_x = {}_1E_x \cdot {}_1E_{x+1} \cdot {}_1E_{x+2} \cdots {}_1E_{x+n-1}$;

(c) Use the first identity to compute the numerical value of ${}_9E_{30}$ from the available tables.

4. (a) To what would the formula for ${}_nE_x$ reduce if (x) were sure to survive the n years?

(b) To what would it reduce if money were unproductive?

(c) To what would it reduce if money were unproductive and (x) were sure to survive the n years?

5. A man now aged 25 has $1000 cash. If he deposits this with an insurance company what sum should he receive at age 45 if he agrees to forfeit all rights in event of death before age 45?

6. Check by computation the values of D_{20}, D_{55}, ${}_{15}E_{25}$, and $1/{}_5E_{50}$ given in the tables.

7. Prove that $D_{x+1} = v \cdot p_x \cdot D_x$.

8. What pure endowment payable at age 65 could a man aged 30 purchase with $2000 cash?

9. Find the present value of a pure endowment

(a) of $1000, due in 30 years and purchased at age 25;

(b) of $500, due in 10 years and purchased at age 60.

10. Compute the values of $_{10}E_{70}$ and $1/_{20}E_{65}$.

13. Life Annuities. A *life annuity* is a set of periodic payments, usually of equal size, payable over a period of years, each payment contingent upon the survival of a designated individual, called the *annuitant*, to the time of payment. The terms, *payment interval, annual rent, term, immediate,* and *due,* are applicable to life annuities in the same manner as to annuities certain. If the annuity is to continue through the entire life of the annuitant, the annuity is called a *whole life* annuity, whereas if the payments cease at the end of a specified time, even though the annuitant be then still living, the annuity is called a *temporary* life annuity. Unless otherwise specified, the words *life annuity* imply a whole life annuity, rather than a temporary life annuity. It is obvious that a pure endowment is a special case of a temporary life annuity, that is, a temporary life annuity having only one payment.

Annuities are classified according to the time at which the term begins with respect to the present age of the annuitant. If the term begins at the present age of the annuitant, the annuity is called *ordinary;* if the term begins sometime in the future, the annuity is *deferred;* whereas if the term of the annuity began sometime in the past, the annuity is called a *foreborne* annuity.

14. Whole Life Annuity. Suppose that l_x persons, all of age x, desire to provide a fund from which amounts are to be withdrawn each year sufficient to pay a dollar to each survivor, the payments to continue as long as there are any survivors. At the end of the first year there will be l_{x+1} survivors according to the mortality table and l_{x+1} dollars will be needed then, or $v \cdot l_{x+1}$ dollars now. Similarly, at the end of the second year there will be l_{x+2} survivors and $v^2 \cdot l_{x+2}$ dollars now will be needed to take care of the payments to be made at that time. Likewise $v^3 \cdot l_{x+3}$ dollars now will be necessary to take care of the payments to be made to the survivors at the end of the third year, and so on to the end of the mortality table. If we denote by a_x the contribution to be made by each individual into the fund at age x, equating the total contributions to the total present value of the payments, we obtain

$$l_x \cdot a_x = vl_{x+1} + v^2l_{x+2} + v^3l_{x+3} + \cdots + v^{\omega-x}l_\omega,$$

and, upon dividing by l_x,

$$(17) \qquad a_x = \frac{vl_{x+1} + v^2l_{x+2} + v^3l_{x+3} + \cdots + v^{\omega-x}l_\omega}{l_x}.$$

It is to be noted that each individual of the above group receives from the fund one dollar payable at the end of each year as long as he survives, and that a_x represents the present value or *single premium* which he pays for this benefit, which in this case constitutes a *whole life annuity immediate*.

Multiplying equation (17) in numerator and denominator by v^x, we obtain

$$(18) \qquad a_x = \frac{v^{x+1}l_{x+1} + v^{x+2}l_{x+2} + v^{x+3}l_{x+3} + \cdots + v^\omega l_\omega}{v^x l_x},$$

or

$$a_x = \frac{D_{x+1} + D_{x+2} + D_{x+3} + \cdots + D_\omega}{D_x},$$

since $D_x = v^x l_x$; $D_{x+1} = v^{x+1}l_{x+1}$, etc.

Represent by the commutation * symbol N_x the following

* The symbol N_x (called "open bar N") is used to distinguish the above definition from the N_x used in English textbooks and defined by the relationship

$$N_x = D_{x+1} + D_{x+2} + \cdots.$$

This fact should be borne in mind when referring to an unfamiliar mortality table.

The reason for the introduction of commutation symbols will be clarified sum

$$N_x = D_x + D_{x+1} + D_{x+2} + \cdots + D_\omega,$$

the sum being taken to the limiting age of the table. For example,

$$N_{25} = D_{25} + D_{26} + D_{27} + \cdots + D_\omega,$$
$$N_{30} = D_{30} + D_{31} + D_{32} + \cdots + D_\omega.$$

Replacing the numerator of the right member of equation (18) by N_{x+1}, we find

$$(19) \qquad a_x = \frac{N_{x+1}}{D_x}.$$

The preceding method of derivation is commonly referred to as the "mutual fund method."

The single premium for a whole life annuity immediate, a_x, can be obtained also by considering it as the sum of a series of pure endowments due at the end of one year, two years, three years, and so on. Using this method, we find the

by the following comparison. Let us suppose that the numerical values of life annuities immediate are required at ages 30 and 31 based upon the American Experience Table. Applying formula (17), we have

$$a_{30} = \frac{vl_{31} + v^2 l_{32} + v^3 l_{33} + \cdots + v^{65} l_{95}}{l_{30}},$$

$$a_{31} = \frac{vl_{32} + v^2 l_{33} + v^3 l_{30} + \cdots + v^{64} l_{95}}{l_{31}}.$$

A total of 129 multiplications are required to find these numerical values, 65 in the first numerator and 64 in the second numerator, since there are no duplicates. Assuming that the values of the commutation symbols D_x and N_x are not available, and using formula (19), we obtain

$$a_{30} = \frac{D_{31} + D_{32} + \cdots + D_{95}}{D_{30}}, \qquad a_{31} = \frac{D_{32} + D_{33} + \cdots + D_{95}}{D_{31}},$$

which would require a total of only 65 multiplications, since all of the terms in the second numerator are duplicates of terms in the first. The difference between the two formulas would be further emphasized if a larger number of annuities were to be calculated. Hence, commutation symbols not only give a convenient means of expressing the rather cumbersome formula (17), but they also shorten to a large extent the number of numerical calculations to be made.

formula

$$a_x = {}_1E_x + {}_2E_x + {}_3E_x + \cdots + {}_{\omega-x}E_x,$$

or

$$a_x = \frac{D_{x+1} + D_{x+2} + D_{x+3} + \cdots + D_\omega}{D_x} = \frac{N_{x+1}}{D_x}.$$

When referring to whole life annuities, the student should note that the only difference between an annuity immediate and an annuity due is the payment made at the beginning of the first year under the latter annuity. All of the other payments under the two types will coincide; hence, if the present value or single premium for a whole life annuity due be represented by a_x, it follows that

$$a_x = 1 + a_x = 1 + \frac{N_{x+1}}{D_x} = \frac{D_x + N_{x+1}}{D_x},$$

or

$$(20) \qquad a_x = \frac{N_x}{D_x}.$$

Table IV gives the values of the whole life annuity due a_x.

EXERCISES—LIST IX

1. Compute the net single premiums for a whole life annuity immediate and a whole life annuity due, of $600 per year, purchased at age 30. At age 50.

2. A man now aged 60 has $10,000 cash. What annuity payment per year, first payment at age 61, can he purchase?

3. A man aged 65 is promised a pension of $500 at the end of each year for as long as he lives. What is the present value of the pension?

4. A man aged 30 agrees to pay a life insurance company $50 at the beginning of each year as long as he lives. What single payment at age 30 is equivalent to this annuity?

5. Derive by means of mutual fund method the formula for the single premium for a whole life annuity due for an individual now aged 30.

6. Show that

(a) $a_x = 1 + v \cdot p_x \cdot a_{x+1};$ (b) $a_{x+1} = \dfrac{(1+i)a_x}{p_x}.$

7. Assuming that the rate of interest is zero, show that $a_x = e_x$.

8. Prove that $a_x < 1/i$.

HINT. $l_x > l_{x+1} > l_{x+2} > \cdots$.

9. Prove algebraically, and by verbal interpretation, the formula

$$a_x = \sum_{n=1}^{\omega-x+1} (a_{\overline{n}|} \cdot {}_{n-1}|q_x).$$

10. Use the identity of problem 6(a) to find l_{20} and l_{21}, if, at 4%,
$a_{20} = 18.662,$ $a_{21} = 18.517,$ $a_{22} = 18.379,$ $l_{22} = 94{,}932.$

15. Temporary and Deferred Life Annuities.   Let $a_{x:\overline{n}|}$
denote * the present value or single premium for a temporary
life annuity due with annual rent \$1, that is, a sequence of
n one dollar payments to be made at the beginning of each
year, each payment being contingent upon the survival of
(x) to receive it. The annuity ceases at the end of n years,
even though (x) be still alive. Such a single premium may
be considered as the sum of the present values of a series of
pure endowments of one dollar, payable at the beginning
of each year for the next n years; hence

$$a_{x:\overline{n}|} = {}_0E_x + {}_1E_x + {}_2E_x + \cdots + {}_{n-1}E_x,$$

or

$$a_{x:\overline{n}|} = \frac{D_x + D_{x+1} + D_{x+2} + \cdots + D_{x+n-1}}{D_x}.$$

Since

$$N_x = D_x + D_{x+1} + \cdots + D_{x+n-1} + D_{x+n} + \cdots + D_\omega,$$
$$N_{x+n} = \qquad\qquad\qquad\qquad\qquad D_{x+n} + \cdots + D_\omega,$$

we have, upon subtraction,

$$N_x - N_{x+n} = D_x + D_{x+1} + \cdots + D_{x+n-1},$$

---

* Some textbooks upon this subject use the symbols $|_n a_x$ and $_n|_m a_x$ in place
of $a_{x:\overline{n}|}$ and $_n|a_{x:\overline{m}|}$, respectively. The notation used by the authors has the
advantage of producing symmetrical relationships in succeeding chapters.

and hence

$$(21) \qquad a_{x:\overline{n}|} = \frac{N_x - N_{x+n}}{D_x}.$$

Numerical values of $a_{x:\overline{n}|}$ are given in Table IX for selected values of n.

Let $_n|a_x$ denote the present value or single premium for a deferred whole life annuity due with annual rent $1, that is, a sequence of one dollar payments to be made at the end of n years, $n + 1$ years, and so on, each payment contingent upon the survival of (x) to receive it. There are no payments made during the deferred period of n years but they continue at the beginning of each succeeding year as long as (x) is alive.

It is evident that

$$_n|a_x = {_n}E_x + {_{n+1}}E_x + {_{n+2}}E_x + \cdots + {_{\omega-x}}E_x,$$

or

$$_n|a_x = \frac{D_{x+n} + D_{x+n+1} + D_{x+n+2} + \cdots + D_\omega}{D_x},$$

and hence

$$(22) \qquad _n|a_x = \frac{N_{x+n}}{D_x}.$$

Let $_n|a_{x:\overline{m}|}$ denote the present value or single premium for a deferred temporary life annuity due of annual rent $1, that is, a sequence of one dollar payments payable at the end of n years, $n + 1$ years, $\cdots$, $n + m - 1$ years, each payment contingent upon the survival of (x) to receive it. This is the most general type of life annuity, since any sequence of payments in the future could be reproduced by giving the quantities n and m suitable values. Considering this single premium as the sum of a sequence of pure endowments, one has

$$_n|a_{x:\overline{m}|} = {}_nE_x + {}_{n+1}E_x + {}_{n+2}E_x + \cdots + {}_{n+m-1}E_x,$$

or

$$_n|a_{x:\overline{m}|} = \frac{D_{x+n} + D_{x+n+1} + D_{x+n+2} + \cdots + D_{x+n+m-1}}{D_x},$$

and hence

$$(23) \qquad _n|a_{x:\overline{m}|} = \frac{N_{x+n} - N_{x+n+m}}{D_x}.$$

Let $a_{x:\overline{n}|}$, $_n|a_x$ and $_n|a_{x:\overline{m}|}$ represent the present values of the corresponding annuities immediate. Comparing the dates upon which the payments are to be made, we observe that

$$a_{x:\overline{n}|} = {}_1|a_{x:\overline{n}|} = \frac{N_{x+1} - N_{x+n+1}}{D_x},$$

$$_n|a_x = {}_{n+1}|a_x = \frac{N_{x+n+1}}{D_x},$$

$$_n|a_{x:\overline{m}|} = {}_{n+1}|a_{x:\overline{m}|} = \frac{N_{x+n+1} - N_{x+n+m+1}}{D_x}.$$

DIAGRAM ILLUSTRATING ANNUITY PAYMENTS
On the Assumption that (x) will Die after $n + m$ Years

		x	$x+1$	$x+2$		$x+n-1$	$x+n$	$x+n+1$		$x+n+m$			
a_x	=		1	1	... 1		1	1	1	... 1	1	1	1 ... 1 1
a_x	=1	1	1	... 1		1	1	1	1	... 1	1	1	1 ... 1 1
$a_{x:\overline{n}|}$	=		1	1	... 1		1	1					
$a_{x:\overline{n}	}$	=1	1	1	... 1		1	1					
$_n|a_x$	=							1	... 1	1	1 1	... 1 1	
$_n|a_x$	=						1	1	... 1	1	1 1	... 1 1	
$_n|a_{x:\overline{m}|}$	=							1	... 1	1 1			
$_n|a_{x:\overline{m}|}$	=						1	1	... 1	1			
$_nE_x$	=							1					

EXERCISES—LIST X

1. (a) Prove algebraically the following identities:

$$(1) \qquad {}_n|a_x \quad = {}_nE_x \cdot a_{x+n};$$

$$(2) \qquad a_{x:\overline{m+n}|} = a_{x:\overline{m}|} + {}_mE_x \cdot a_{x+m:\overline{n}|};$$

$$(3) \qquad {}_n|a_{x:\overline{m}|} = {}_nE_x \cdot a_{x+n:\overline{m}|}.$$

(b) Use the identities in (a) to compute from the available tables of a_x, $a_{x:\overline{m}|}$, and ${}_nE_x$ the numerical values of

$$(1) \ {}_{10}|a_{30}; \qquad (2) \ a_{25:\overline{14}|}; \qquad (3) \ {}_4|a_{35:\overline{20}|}.$$

2. Derive the formulas for each of the following by the mutual fund method:

$$\text{(a) } {}_n|a_x; \qquad\qquad\qquad \text{(b) } a_{x:\overline{m}|}.$$

3. Prove the identities:

(a) $a_{x:\overline{m}|} = 1 + a_{x:\overline{n-1}|};$ $\qquad$ (b) ${}_n|a_x = a_x - a_{x:\overline{m}|};$

$$\text{(c) } a_{x:\overline{m}|} = a_x - {}_nE_x \cdot a_{x+n}.$$

4. Show that

(a) $a_{x:\overline{m}|} < a_{\overline{m}|};$ $\qquad\qquad$ (b) ${}_n|a_{x:\overline{m}|} < v^n a_{\overline{m}|}.$

5. An individual aged 35 pays \$5000 to an insurance company in return for a contract to pay him a fixed annual income for life, starting with a payment on his 55th birthday. No payment is to be made by the company if he dies before age 55.

(a) Find the annual income if the company makes no charge for expense.

(b) What will the annual income be if the company deducts 5% of the premium for expenses?

6. A certain life insurance policy calls for the payment of premiums of \$100 at the beginning of each year for twenty years by an individual now aged 34. Find the present value of the premiums.

7. A man aged 20 agrees to pay \$50 at the beginning of each year for as long as he lives. What is the present value of the payments? If the last payment is to be made when the man reaches age 84, what is the present value of the payments?

8. A certain life insurance policy matures when the policyholder is of age 50 and gives him an option of \$10,000 in cash or a sequence of equal payments at the beginning of each year for ten years and as long thereafter as he may live. If he dies during the first ten years the payments are to be continued to his heirs until a total of ten have been made. Find the annual payment under the optional plan.

HINT. The optional plan gives an annuity certain and a life annuity deferred ten years. Hence, if R denotes the annual payment, it follows that

$$R(a_{\overline{10}|} + {}_{10|}a_{50}) = 10,000.$$

9. Fill in the missing quantities in the following table, assuming that $v = 0.9$ (carry computations to three decimal places).

AGE x	l_x	d_x	q_x	p_x	a_x	e_x	$\overset{o}{e}_x$
90	600	100					
91							
92	400			0.75			
93							
94	200		0.50				
95							
96	0						

16. Foreborne Annuity.

Consider a group of l_x individuals forming a fund into which each individual contributes a fixed amount at the beginning of each year for a stated number of years. These contributions are to be invested at compound interest at rate i and at the end of the given period of years the total accumulated fund is to be divided among the survivors. No return is made from the fund when a member dies, but his contributions assist in increasing the amount which each survivor receives. This type of fund is called a *tontine fund*. Each survivor receives what is known as a *foreborne annuity*. We shall consider the problem of determining the amount which each survivor will receive at the end of the stated period, say n years.

Let the share of each survivor at the end of the n year period be denoted by ${}_nu_x$ and assume that each individual contributes one dollar at the beginning of each year. The fund receives l_x dollars at the beginning of the first year, which accumulate to $l_x(1 + i)^n$ at the end of the n years. At the beginning of the second year there will be l_{x+1} lives remaining, each of whom pays a second dollar, and the total accumulation of which at the end of n years will be $l_{x+1}(1 + i)^{n-1}$, and so on until at the beginning of the last year there will be l_{x+n-1} survivors who will contribute a dollar each producing an accumulation of $l_{x+n-1}(1 + i)$ at the end of the n year period. After dividing the total of these accumulated values by the number of survivors at the end of the n year period, we have

$$_nu_x = \frac{l_x(1 + i)^n + l_{x+1}(1 + i)^{n-1} + \cdots + l_{x+n-1}(1 + i)}{l_{x+n}}.$$

Multiplying numerator and denominator by v^{x+n} and reducing to commutation symbols, we obtain

$$_nu_x = \frac{D_x + D_{x+1} + D_{x+2} + \cdots + D_{x+n-1}}{D_{x+n}},$$

and hence

(24) $$_nu_x = \frac{N_x - N_{x+n}}{D_{x+n}}.$$

The symbol $_nu_x$ is frequently referred to as the "accumulated value of the individual survivor's payments with the benefit of interest and survivorship." Formula (24) may also be obtained by setting $a_{x:\overline{n}|}$ (the present value of the payments) equal to the present value of a pure endowment of amount $_nu_x$ due at the end of n years. Thus

$$a_{x:\overline{n}|} = {_nu_x} \cdot {_nE_x},$$

or

$$_nu_x = a_{x:\overline{n}|}\left(\frac{1}{_nE_x}\right) = \frac{N_x - N_{x+n}}{D_{x+n}}.$$

The reciprocal $1/_nE_x$ as used in the above equation appears as an accumulation factor with benefit of interest and survivorship and will be used in this sense in succeeding articles.

When $n = 1$, the notation u_x is usually used instead of $_1u_x$; hence

$$(25) \qquad u_x = \frac{N_x - N_{x+1}}{D_{x+1}} = \frac{D_x}{D_{x+1}}.$$

Numerical values of $_nu_x$ and u_x are shown in Tables X and VI, respectively.

17. General Annuity Formula. It is now possible to set up a general expression for the value, at any time, of a sequence of payments of the same size, where each payment is contingent upon the survival of a designated life. Thus

$$(26) \qquad R \cdot \frac{N_a - N_b}{D_c}$$

gives the value at age c of a series of annual payments of R dollars each, the first payment payable at age a and the last payment payable at age $b - 1$. Whenever the age b is beyond the limiting age of the table the second term in the numerator disappears. The difference $b - a$ indicates the number of the annual payments. By properly choosing the ages a, b, and c, expression (26) may be adapted to reproduce the formulas for a_x, a_x, $a_{x:\overline{n}|}$, $a_{x:\overline{n}|}$, $_n|a_{x:\overline{m}|}$, $_nE_x$, $_nu_x$, and u_x.

EXERCISES—LIST XI

1. A man aged 30 wishes to provide for a life annuity of $1000 per year, first payment to be made when he reaches age 60. What annual payment should he deposit with an insurance company at the beginning of each year for the next thirty years

(a) if his contract specifies that no return of payments will be made in event of his death,

(b) if his contract specifies that, in event of his death prior to age 60, the company will return immediately all of his deposits with interest?

SOLUTION. (a) Under this condition his accumulation at age 60 is the accumulated value of a foreborne annuity. Hence it follows that

$$R \cdot {}_{30}u_{30} = 1000 \cdot a_{60},$$

and, by Tables IV and X,

$$R = \frac{1000a_{60}}{{}_{30}u_{30}} = \frac{1000(11.032399)}{70.14711} = \$157.28.$$

(b) Under this latter condition he receives only the benefit of interest on his deposits prior to age 60, and since the annual payments constitute an annuity due, it follows that

$$R\$\overline{s_{30|}} = 1000a_{60}, \qquad R(s_{\overline{31|}} - 1) = 1000a_{60},$$

and, by Tables IV and I,

$$R = \frac{1000a_{60}}{s_{\overline{31|}} - 1} = \frac{1000(11.032399)}{53.429471} = \$206.49.$$

2. (a) Prove that

$$_{m+n}u_x = {}_{m}u_x \cdot \frac{1}{{}_{n}E_{x+m}} + {}_{n}u_{x+m}.$$

(b) Use the identity in (a) to find the numerical value of $_{17}u_{20}$ from the available tables.

3. Prove that

(a) $$a_{x+1} = (a_x - 1)u_x;$$

(b) $$_{n}u_x = \frac{a_x}{{}_{n}E_x} - a_{x+n};$$

(c) $$a_x = vp_x(u_x + a_{x+1}).$$

4. A man now aged 20 has an annuity of \$5000 a year due him at ages 25, 26, 27, 28, and 29, each payment contingent upon his survival to that age. He desires to trade these payments for a life annuity beginning at the present time. What will be the annual rent of the new annuity?

5. An individual now aged 40 desires to purchase a deferred life annuity of \$1000 a year, first payment to occur at the end of twenty years. He wishes to buy this annuity by means of equal annual premiums at the beginning of each year for the next ten years. If no return of premiums is to be made in event of his death at any time, calculate the net premium he is to pay.

6. A boy aged 17 is to receive a legacy of \$10,000 if living on his 25th birthday. He wishes to change this to an income payable at the end of each of the next four years, if living, first payment at age 18. Express the annual rent of the new annuity in terms of commutation symbols.

7. A man aged 35 has an income of \$10,000 payable annually at the end of each year to his estate for the next ten years whether he lives or dies. He desires to exchange this for a deferred life annuity, first payment at age 65. What will be the annual rent of this annuity?

8. Express in terms of commutation symbols the present value of a life annuity due on the life of an individual now aged 30 providing for a sequence of payments of $50 each for the first ten years, then increasing to $100 each year thereafter.

9. A man aged 30 wishes to provide for a life annuity of $1000 per year, first payment at age 50. If he desires no return of payments in event of his death, what annual payment at the beginning of each year for the next twenty years should he deposit with an insurance company?

10. Compute the present value of a temporary life annuity due on the life of an individual now aged 30 providing for a sequence of payments of $500 a year for fifteen years followed by a sequence of ten payments of $1000 each year.

11. Show that $_nu_x > \$_{\overline{n}|}$ and explain verbally why this inequality must be true.

18. Increasing Life Annuities. Consider an increasing life annuity due consisting of a payment of $1 at the beginning of the first year, $2 at the beginning of the second year, $3 at the beginning of the third year, and so on, the payments increasing by a dollar a year and contingent upon the survival of a designated individual (x). The present value or single premium, $(Ia)_x$, of such an annuity consists of the sum of the present values of a series of increasing pure endowments; hence

$$(Ia)_x = 1 \cdot {}_0E_x + 2 \cdot {}_1E_x + 3 \cdot {}_2E_x + \cdots + (\omega - x + 1)_{\omega-x}E_x,$$

$$= \frac{D_x + 2D_{x+1} + 3D_{x+2} + \cdots + (\omega - x + 1)D_\omega}{D_x}.$$

Since

$$
\begin{aligned}
N_x &= D_x + D_{x+1} + D_{x+2} + D_{x+3} + \cdots + D_\omega \\
N_{x+1} &= \phantom{D_x + {}} D_{x+1} + D_{x+2} + D_{x+3} + \cdots + D_\omega \\
N_{x+2} &= \phantom{D_x + D_{x+1} + {}} D_{x+2} + D_{x+3} + \cdots + D_\omega \\
N_{x+3} &= \phantom{D_x + D_{x+1} + D_{x+2} + {}} D_{x+3} + \cdots + D_\omega
\end{aligned}
$$

and so on to the end of the table, the sum of these equations yields

$$N_x + N_{x+1} + N_{x+2} + N_{x+3} + \cdots + N_\omega = D_x + 2D_{x+1} + \\ 3D_{x+2} + 4D_{x+3} + \cdots + (\omega - x + 1)D_\omega.$$

If we define the commutation symbol

$$S_x = N_x + N_{x+1} + N_{x+2} + N_{x+3} + \cdots + N_\omega,$$

then the single premium for the increasing life annuity due can be written

$$(27) \qquad\qquad (Ia)_x = \frac{S_x}{D_x}.$$

EXERCISES—LIST XII

1. A man now aged 30 has a temporary life annuity with successive payments of $500, $450, $400, $350, $300, and $250, the first payment to be made immediately. Compute the present value.

SOLUTION. The successive payments constitute a series of six pure endowments due at the beginning of each of the next six years. Hence, if K represents their present value, we have

$$K = 500_0E_{30} + 450_1E_{30} + 400_2E_{30} + 350_3E_{30} + 300_4E_{30} + 250_5E_{30},$$
$$= 50 \frac{10D_{30} + 9D_{31} + 8D_{32} + 7D_{33} + 6D_{34} + 5D_{35}}{D_{30}}.$$

Upon adding the six equations

$$\begin{aligned} 5(D_{30} + D_{31} + D_{32} + D_{33} + D_{34} + D_{35}) &= 5(N_{30} - N_{36}) \\ D_{30} + D_{31} + D_{32} + D_{33} + D_{34} &= (N_{30} - N_{35}) \\ D_{30} + D_{31} + D_{32} + D_{33} &= (N_{30} - N_{34}) \\ D_{30} + D_{31} + D_{32} &= (N_{30} - N_{33}) \\ D_{30} + D_{31} &= (N_{30} - N_{32}) \\ D_{30} &= (N_{30} - N_{31}), \end{aligned}$$

we obtain

$$10D_{30} + 9D_{31} + 8D_{32} + 7D_{33} + 6D_{34} + 5D_{35} \\ = 10N_{30} - (N_{31} + N_{32} + N_{33} + N_{34} + N_{35} + 5N_{36}) \\ = 10N_{30} - (S_{31} - S_{36}) - 5N_{36}.$$

Hence, using Table III, we have,

$$K = 50 \, \frac{10N_{30} - (S_{31} - S_{36}) - 5N_{36}}{D_{30}}$$

$$= 50 \, \frac{10(596,803.64) - (8,800,553.5 - 6,248,356.9) - 5(432,326.51)}{30,440.784}$$

$$= \$2060.08.$$

2. Show that the present value of an increasing life annuity due payable on the life of (x) is

$$\frac{hN_x + kS_{x+1}}{D_x},$$

if the first payment of h is made immediately, and the succeeding annual payments increase by k per year.

3. Show that if the number of payments in the increasing life annuity due be limited to n, the single premium becomes

$$(Ia)_{x:\overline{n}|} = \frac{S_x - S_{x+n} - n \cdot N_{x+n}}{D_x}.$$

4. A man now aged 35 has a temporary life annuity with successive annual payments of $10, 8, 6, 4, 2, 4, 6, 8, and 10, the first payment to be made immediately. Compute the present value.

5. Express in terms of commutation symbols the present value of each of the following:

(a) Life annuity to a man aged 24 beginning at once with a payment of $10 and increasing by $1 a year until a payment of $25 has been reached, after which the annuity payment remains constant.

(b) Life annuity to a man now aged 30 beginning with an initial payment of $100 at once decreasing by $5 a year until the payment becomes zero.

6. Describe the annuity whose present value is represented by each of the following:

(a) $\dfrac{S_{x+1}}{D_x}$; 　(b) $\dfrac{S_{x+1} - S_{x+n+1}}{D_x}$; 　(c) $\dfrac{S_{x+1} - S_{x+n+1} - n \cdot N_{x+n+1}}{D_x}$.

19. Annuities Payable More than Once per Year. Life insurance and life annuity contracts often provide that the periodical payments shall be made more frequently than once a year. Life insurance premiums are often payable semi-annually or quarterly, industrial insurance premiums are payable weekly, and pensions in many cases are payable monthly. It is necessary therefore to consider the present values of annuities payable m times per year, where m is any given integer. The symbol $a_x^{(m)}$ is used to denote the present value of a life annuity due with annual rent of one dollar payable in m installments of $1/m$ each, the first installment of $1/m$ to be made immediately, and the succeeding installments to be made at the beginning of each succeeding period of $1/m$ years for as long as (x) is alive. Upon considering this annuity as a sequence of pure endowments, one has

$$a_x^{(m)} = \frac{1}{m}(1 + {}_{1/m}E_x + {}_{2/m}E_x + {}_{3/m}E_x + \cdots),$$

or

$$a_x^{(m)} = \frac{1}{m}(1 + v^{1/m} \cdot {}_{1/m}p_x + v^{2/m} \cdot {}_{2/m}p_x + v^{3/m} \cdot {}_{3/m}p_x + \cdots).$$

The evaluation of this expression would ordinarily involve a great amount of arithmetic computation. Moreover, the mortality table gives no information as to the probabilities of an individual living fractional parts of a year, and hence it is impossible to obtain the exact value of $a_x^{(m)}$. However, an approximation satisfactory for most purposes can be obtained.

Consider the two identities:

$$_0|a_x = a_x - 0, \qquad {}_1|a_x = a_x - 1.$$

Linear interpolation between these values for the deferred life annuity ${}_{1/m}|a_x$ yields

$$_{\frac{1}{m}}\Big|a_x = a_x - \frac{1}{m}.$$

Similarly, by interpolation,

$$_{\frac{2}{m}}\Big|a_x = a_x - \frac{2}{m},$$

and, in general,

$$_{\frac{k}{m}}\Big|a_x = a_x - \frac{k}{m}.$$

Suppose that we have m annuities, each of annual rent one dollar, and each payable once per year, the first payments of which fall due at the ends of $0, 1/m, 2/m, \cdots, (m-1)/m$ years, respectively. Together these annuities form an annuity due with annual rent of m dollars, payable m times per year. Hence, the sum of the present values of these annuities will be $m \cdot a_x^{(m)}$; it follows that

$$m \cdot a_x^{(m)} = \left[a_x + \left(a_x - \frac{1}{m} \right) + \left(a_x - \frac{2}{m} \right) + \cdots + \left(a_x - \frac{m-1}{m} \right) \right].$$

The right member of this equation is the sum of an arithmetical progression with a common difference of $-1/m$. Summing up the series, we have

$$m \cdot a_x^{(m)} = m \cdot a_x - \frac{m(m-1)}{2m},$$

and hence, dividing by m, we have, approximately,

$$(28) \qquad a_x^{(m)} = a_x - \frac{m-1}{2m}.$$

If $a_x^{(m)}$ denotes the present value of a life annuity immediate with annual rent one dollar, payable m times per year, then it follows that

$$a_x^{(m)} = a_x^{(m)} - \frac{1}{m} = a_x - \frac{m+1}{2m},$$

or, approximately,

$$(29) \qquad a_x^{(m)} = a_x + \frac{m-1}{2m}.$$

As special cases of formulas (28) and (29), we have the following approximations:

$$a_x^{(2)} = a_x - \tfrac{1}{4}, \qquad a_x^{(2)} = a_x + \tfrac{1}{4},$$
$$a_x^{(4)} = a_x - \tfrac{3}{8}, \qquad a_x^{(4)} = a_x + \tfrac{3}{8},$$
$$a_x^{(12)} = a_x - \tfrac{11}{24}, \qquad a_x^{(12)} = a_x + \tfrac{11}{24}.$$

Similarly, for the temporary life annuity due, we may write

$$a_{x:\overline{n}|}^{(m)} = a_x^{(m)} - {}_n|a_x^{(m)} = a_x^{(m)} - {}_nE_x\, a_{x+n}^{(m)}$$

$$= a_x - \frac{m-1}{2m} - {}_nE_x\left(a_{x+n} - \frac{m-1}{2m}\right)$$

$$= [a_x - {}_nE_x\, a_{x+n}] - \frac{m-1}{2m}(1 - {}_nE_x);$$

hence we have, approximately,

$$(30) \qquad a_{x:\overline{n}|}^{(m)} = a_{x:\overline{n}|} - \frac{m-1}{2m}(1 - {}_nE_x).$$

EXERCISES—LIST XIII

1. Compute the present value of an annuity of $500 semi-annually for the life of an individual now age 25:

(a) when the payments are made at the beginning of each six months,

(b) when the payments are made at the end of each six months.

2. The value of a life annuity of $100 a year to be paid at the end of each year for the lifetime of a certain individual is $1798.54. What is the present value of an annuity of the same annual rent, if the payments are made at the end of each month?

3. A life annuity contract provides for the payment of $100 per annum for the life of the annuitant, first payment at age 60. If, upon attaining age 60, the annuitant desires payments at the beginning of each month, what would be the equitable amount of each monthly payment? If the payments are to be made at the beginning of each quarter, what would be the equitable quarterly payment?

4. (a) The symbol $a_{\overline{n}|}^{(m)}$ is used to denote the present value of an annuity certain due with annual rent one dollar, payable m times per year in installments of $1/m$. By considering an individual who is *certain* to live n years, show that formula (30) can be written in the form

$$a_{\overline{n}|}^{(m)} = a_{\overline{n}|} - \frac{m-1}{2m}(1 - v^n), \text{ approximately.}$$

(b) Using the result of part (a), solve the following problem: What quarterly payment at the beginning of each three months for ten years is equivalent to an annual payment of $100 at the beginning of each year for the same period, assuming the payments are certain to be made?

5. Show that

$$_n\big|a_x^{(m)} = {_nE_x}\left(a_{x+n} - \frac{m-1}{2m}\right), \text{ approximately:}$$

6. Show that

   (a) $a_{x:\overline{n}|}^{(2)} = \tfrac{1}{4}(3a_{x:\overline{n}|} + a_{x:\overline{n}|})$, approximately;

   (b) $a_{x:\overline{n}|}^{(4)} = \tfrac{1}{8}(5a_{x:\overline{n}|} + 3a_{x:\overline{n}|})$, approximately.

7. If $_nu_x^{(m)}$ represents the accumulated value of a foreborne annuity of annual rent one dollar, payable m times per year, show that

$$_nu_x^{(m)} = {_nu_x} - \frac{m-1}{2m} \cdot \left(\frac{1}{_nE_x} - 1\right), \text{ approximately.}$$

8. If $(Ia)_x^{(m)}$ denotes the present value of an increasing life annuity due, payable m times per year, with annual rent of one dollar in the first year, two dollars in the second year, three dollars in the third year, and so on for the life of an individual now aged (x), show that

$$(Ia)_x^{(m)} = (Ia)_x - \frac{m-1}{2m}\, a_x, \text{ approximately.}$$

REVIEW EXERCISE—LIST XIV

1. A whole life annuity immediate on the life of (x) provides for a sequence of payments of (1.035) at the end of one year, $(1.035)^2$ at the end of the second year, $(1.035)^3$ at the end of the third year, and so on. Show that the present value of this annuity at $3\frac{1}{2}\%$ is e_x.

2. Show that the present value of a perpetuity of one dollar per annum, first payment to be made at the end of the year in which (x) dies, is $1/i - a_x$.

3. A is aged 30 and B is aged 40. They wish to contribute equally to a charity. A promises to pay $500 a year on each of his birthdays from the 30th to 44th, inclusive. B agrees to pay R dollars if and when he attains age 45. Find the value of R.

4. Find in commutation symbols an expression for a_{30} where the interest rate is to be 4% for the first ten years and 5% thereafter.

5. Compute the present value at age 30 of a whole life annuity immediate having an annual rent of $120 payable in equal installments (a) annually, (b) semi-annually, (c) quarterly, and (d) monthly.

6. Show that

   (a) $_nu_x = (_{n-1}u_x + 1)u_{x+n-1}.$

   (b) $a_{x+1} = (a_x - 1)u_x.$

7. A man aged x offers a single premium of

$$\frac{a_{x-n} - a_{x-n:\overline{2n}|}}{{}_nE_{x-n}}$$

for a deferred life annuity, first payment at age $x + n$. Find the annual rent of the annuity.

8. Prove

$$_r\Big|a_{x:\overline{n}|}^{(m)} = {}_r\Big|a_{x:\overline{n}|} - \frac{m-1}{2m}({}_rE_x - {}_{n+r}E_x), \text{ approximately.}$$

9. If $(Ia)_{x:\overline{n}|}^{(m)}$ denotes the present value of an increasing temporary life annuity due, payable m times per year, with annual rent of one dollar in the first year, two dollars in the second year, three dollars in the third year, and so on until finally n dollars is paid during the *nth* year, show that

$$(Ia)_{x:\overline{n}|}^{(m)} = (Ia)_{x:\overline{n}|} - \frac{m-1}{2m}[a_{x:\overline{n}|} - n \cdot {}_nE_x], \text{ approximately.}$$

10. A beneficiary now aged 50 is offered one of the following options:

(a) \$10,000 in cash, or

(b) Equal payments at the beginning of each month for as long as she lives, or

(c) Equal payments at the beginning of each month for as long as she lives, the payments in any event to be made for at least 120 months.

Compute the monthly payment under options (b) and (c).

HINT. See Exercise 8, List X, and Exercises 4(a) and 5, List XIII.

CHAPTER III

NET PREMIUMS

20. Introduction. Life insurance is on a sound basis only when a large number of individuals are insured under one organization or company, so that individual losses may be distributed over the whole group according to some scientific principle of mutuality. When an individual is insured by a company, he and the company agree to a written contract, called a *policy*. In the policy the *insured*, or *policyholder*, agrees to make certain payments to the company. These payments are usually referred to as *gross* or *office premiums*. In consideration of the premiums paid to the company by the insured, the company in turn agrees to pay a stipulated sum of money, called the *face* amount of insurance, if certain events occur. The person to whom the face amount of insurance is to be paid is called the *beneficiary*. The *policy date* or *date of issue* is the date upon which the insurance contract is made, and the successive years after this date are called *policy years*. Most life insurance companies charge gross premiums which are determined by the age the *insured* attained or will attain on his birthday nearest to the date of issue. This *age nearest birthday* is referred to as the *age at issue*.

The fundamental problem is to determine the premiums which should be charged a policyholder in return for the promised benefits under his policy. Every company adopts a mortality table and an assumed rate of interest on invested funds as the basis for this computation. Some companies use the American Experience Table for this purpose, while others use the American Men Table. Usually a rate of interest from 3 to 4 1/2%, compounded annually, is assumed.

The *net* premiums for a policy are those whose total present value is equal to the present value of the policy benefits under the following assumptions: (a) the benefits under the policy will be paid at the ends of the policy years in which they fall due; (b) the company's invested funds will earn interest at exactly the assumed rate; and (c) the deaths among the policyholders will occur at exactly the rate given by the adopted mortality table. Under these assumptions, if a company were run without profit or expense, it could afford to issue policies in return for these net premiums. Whenever the net premiums are assumed to be the same for all policy years in which the premium is paid, the premiums are called *net level premiums*.

The actual gross premium charged by the company is the net premium plus a certain amount, called *loading*, which provides for the expenses of the company and for the added disbursements due to the violation of the conditions (a), (b), and (c). Attention will be given later to the problem of computing gross premiums, while the present chapter will be devoted entirely to the discussion of net premiums and related questions. It should be noted that a policyholder invariably agrees to pay, in addition to the loading, a series of net premiums whose present value is equal to the present value of all of the policy benefits. Thus, a policyholder always agrees to pay for what he receives under the policy, and if the premium for one policy is less than that for another policy, but payable for the same period of time, it follows that the benefits under the first policy have a smaller present value. The question of which policy is best for a given individual is largely a question of fitting the type of benefits and the size of the premium to the individual's needs and resources.

21. Whole Life Insurance. When a policy provides for the payment of all of the insured's premium obligations in one installment, this installment is payable immediately on the policy date and is called the *single premium* for the policy. The present value of all benefits under the assumptions (a), (b), and (c) of the previous section is called the *net single premium*.

A *whole life insurance* may be defined as a benefit consisting of a fixed sum to be paid to the beneficiary at the time of the death of the insured. A policy containing this provision is called a *whole life* policy. Similarly, the net single premium for a whole life insurance is the present value, under a definite assumption regarding mortality and interest, of the face amount of the policy payable at the end of the year in which the death of the insured occurs.

Let A_x denote the net single premium for a whole life insurance of one dollar on the life of (x), that is, the present value of one dollar to be paid at the end of the year in which (x) dies. If a company insured l_x individuals, each of age x, on the same policy date, the total single premium collections would be $l_x \cdot A_x$. During the first policy year, d_x deaths would occur among this group and d_x dollars would be payable at the end of the first year to beneficiaries. In order to meet this obligation vd_x dollars would be needed now. During the second policy year d_{x+1} deaths would occur and $v^2 d_{x+1}$ dollars would be needed now to care for the payments to beneficiaries; during the third year d_{x+2} deaths would occur and $v^3 d_{x+2}$ dollars would be needed now, and so on until all of the l_x individuals, originally insured, had died. Equating the total net premiums collected by the company to the total present value of the benefits, we have

$$l_x A_x = vd_x + v^2 d_{x+1} + v^3 d_{x+2} + v^4 d_{x+3} + \cdots + v^{\omega-x+1} d_\omega,$$

or

$$A_x = \frac{vd_x + v^2 d_{x+1} + v^3 d_{x+2} + v^4 d_{x+3} + \cdots + v^{\omega-x+1} d_\omega}{l_x}.$$

Multiplying numerator and denominator of the right member of this equation by v^x, we find

$$A_x = \frac{v^{x+1}d_x + v^{x+2}d_{x+1} + v^{x+3}d_{x+2} + v^{x+4}d_{x+3} + \cdots + v^{\omega+1}d_\omega}{v^x l_x}.$$

Let the product $v^{x+1}d_x$ be represented by the commutation symbol C_x. For example:

$$C_{25} = v^{26}d_{25}; \qquad C_{30} = v^{31}d_{30}; \text{ etc.}$$

Introducing the commutation * symbols C_x, C_{x+1}, C_{x+2}, $\cdots$ into the expression for A_x, we have

$$A_x = \frac{C_x + C_{x+1} + C_{x+2} + C_{x+3} + \cdots + C_\omega}{D_x}.$$

Denote by the commutation symbol M_x the sum

$$M_x = C_x + C_{x+1} + C_{x+2} + C_{x+3} + \cdots + C_\omega.$$
Thus $M_{25} = C_{25} + C_{26} + C_{27} + \cdots + C_\omega,$
$$M_{30} = C_{30} + C_{31} + C_{32} + \cdots + C_\omega.$$

It follows immediately that

(31) $$A_x = \frac{M_x}{D_x}.$$

Similarly, the net single premium for a whole life insurance of R on the life of (x) is

$$R \cdot A_x = R \cdot \frac{M_x}{D_x}.$$

Values of the single premium A_x and its reciprocal are given in Table IV, whereas values of the commutation symbols C_x and M_x are to be found in Table III.

* The student should note that these new commutation symbols are introduced not only for simplicity in representation, but also because they materially reduce the number of necessary numerical calculations.

EXERCISES—LIST XV

1. Verify the entries in the tables of C_x and M_x at ages 95, 94, and 93. Verify the entries in the table of A_x at ages 20, 35, 50.

2. Find the net single premium for a whole life insurance of $4000 on the life of a man (a) aged 20; (b) aged 40; (c) aged 85.

3. How much whole life insurance can a man aged 40 purchase with $2000 cash, assuming that the gross and net premiums are the same?

4. Derive by the mutual fund method an expression in terms of commutation symbols for the present value of a whole life insurance of amount R issued at age 30.

5. Prove that $A_x = v(q_x + p_x A_{x+1})$.

6. Show that $A_x u_x = A_{x+1} + q_x/p_x$.

7. Show that

$$\text{(a)} \quad p_x = \frac{1 - (1+i)A_x}{1 - A_{x+1}}, \qquad \text{(b)} \quad q_x = \frac{(1+i)A_x - A_{x+1}}{1 - A_{x+1}}.$$

22. Relations between Single Premiums.

Certain fundamental relations exist between the two sets of commutation symbols and also between A_x and a_x. Since

$$C_x = v^{x+1} \cdot d_x = v^{x+1}(l_x - l_{x+1}),$$
$$C_x = v \cdot v^x \cdot l_x - v^{x+1}l_{x+1},$$

it follows that

$$(32) \qquad C_x = v \cdot D_x - D_{x+1}.$$

Likewise,

$$C_{x+1} = vD_{x+1} - D_{x+2},$$
$$C_{x+2} = vD_{x+2} - D_{x+3},$$

and so on, to the end of the table. Adding these results by columns, we obtain

$$(33) \qquad M_x = v \cdot N_x - N_{x+1}.$$

Dividing both members of equation (33) by D_x, we have immediately

$$(34) \qquad A_x = va_x - a_x.$$

If we denote the difference $1 - v$ by d, called the *rate of discount*, then since $a_x = a_x - 1$, equation (34) may be written in the form

$$(35) \qquad A_x = 1 - da_x.$$

It is evident from these relations that values of C_x and M_x could, if necessary, be obtained directly from a table of values of D_x and N_x without recourse to the original mortality table, and values of A_x could be obtained from a table of values of either a_x or a_x.

Formulas (34) and (35) can be proved by verbal interpretations which are highly instructive. Thus equation (34) may be substantiated as follows: Consider an annuity of v payable at the beginning of each year which (x) enters, and a second annuity of 1 payable at the end of each year which (x) completes. The first annuity contains one payment more than the second annuity, namely, the payment of v at the beginning of the year in which (x) dies. Since a payment of v at the beginning of any year is equivalent to a payment of 1 at the end of that year, the difference between these two annuities is represented by the payment of v at the beginning of the year in which (x) dies. This payment of v will accumulate to 1 at the end of the year in which (x) dies; hence the difference between the present values of the two annuities is the present value of 1 payable at the end of the year in which (x) dies, or A_x.

Similarly equation (35) can be verbally interpreted as follows: Suppose that one dollar were invested for the lifetime of (x) at the rate i. The interest of i payable at the end of any year is equivalent to iv or d payable at the beginning of that year. Thus the original investment of one dollar produces an annuity due of d for the lifetime of (x) and returns the principal of one dollar at the end of the year in which (x) dies. Upon equating present values, equation (35) results.

Interpret each of the following equations verbally:

1. $v^n = 1 - d \cdot a_{\overline{n}|}$.
2. $v^n = v \cdot a_{\overline{n}|} - a_{\overline{n-1}|}$.
3. $l_x(1 + i)A_x = d_x + l_{x+1}A_{x+1}$.
4. Show that $M_x = D_x - dN_x$.
5. Prove $A_x = v(1 - ia_x) = v - (1 - v)a_x = v - da_x$.

23. Annual Premiums. Most policies commonly issued by life insurance companies provide for the payment of premiums in equal annual installments. These annual premiums are payable at the beginning of each policy year and may continue throughout the entire lifetime of the insured or they may be limited to a specified period of years, called the *premium payment period*. Thus, a policy containing a whole life insurance benefit may be classified as: (a) *ordinary life*, where the annual premium is payable throughout the entire lifetime of the insured, or (b) *limited payment life*, in which the annual premium is payable only for a limited number of years, usually ten, fifteen or twenty years. Premiums for limited payment life policies are, of course, higher than those for ordinary life policies. A single premium life policy is a special case of a limited payment life policy, that is, a limited payment life policy with just one premium.

Let P_x denote the net level annual premium for an ordinary life policy issued at age x. These annual premiums form a life annuity due, whose present value is $P_x \cdot a_x$. Since the present value of these premiums is, by definition, equal to the net single premium for the benefit provided by the policy, we have

$$P_x \cdot a_x = A_x,$$

and hence

(36) $$P_x = \frac{A_x}{a_x},$$

or, by § 14,

$$P_x = \frac{M_x}{N_x}.$$

Another form for P_x can be found by replacing A_x by $1 - da_x$ in equation (36). In this manner, we find

(37) $$P_x = \frac{1 - da_x}{a_x} = \frac{1}{a_x} - d.$$

Let $_nP_x$ denote the net level annual premium for a limited payment life policy, with a premium payment period of n years. Such a policy is usually referred to as an n payment life policy. In this case the premiums form a temporary life annuity due. Equating their present value to the net single premium, A_x, we have

$$_nP_x\, a_{x:\overline{n}|} = A_x,$$

and hence

(38) $$_nP_x = \frac{A_x}{a_{x:\overline{n}|}},$$

or, by § 15,

$$_nP_x = \frac{M_x}{N_x - N_{x+n}}$$

It should be noted that all formulas for premiums which have been considered are net premiums providing for a benefit of one dollar. Premiums for other amounts of insurance could be found by multiplying the premium for a benefit of one dollar by the face amount of insurance. Table V shows the numerical values of the net premiums for the ordinary life, nineteen payment life, and twenty payment life policies.

EXERCISES—LIST XVII

1. Find to the nearest cent the numerical value of the net annual premium for each of the following policies issued at age 30, the amount of insurance in each case to be $1000:

(a) five payment life,

(b) ten payment life,

(c) thirty payment life.

2. Check the numerical value of P_{45} given in Table V, by means of (37).

3. What is the net annual premium for a twenty payment life policy for $5000 issued at age 60? Age 20? Age 15?

4. Prove that

$$\text{(a) } A_x = \frac{P_x}{P_x + d}, \qquad\qquad \text{(b) } P_x = \frac{dA_x}{1 - A_x}.$$

5. Show that

$$P_x = \frac{vq_x + P_{x+1} \cdot a_x}{a_x}.$$

24. Term Insurance.

A term insurance may be defined as the benefit consisting of a fixed sum to be paid to the beneficiary at the time of the death of the insured, provided that death occurs within a limited period. It should be noted that no payment is made by the company in event that the insured survives the limited period. Thus, a ten year term insurance gives no benefit unless the insured dies within ten years. Let $A^1_{x:\overline{n}|}$ denote the net single premium for an n year term insurance of one dollar on the life of (x). The first subscript in the symbol indicates the present age (age at issue) of the insured, while the second subscript indicates the temporary period during which the insurance is effective. The mark "1" above the age indicates that the benefit is payable only if the insured dies before the n years expire.*

If a company were to issue n year term policies to each of l_x individuals, all of age x, the total net single premiums collected immediately by the company would aggregate $l_x \cdot A^1_{x:\overline{n}|}$. As in the case of whole life insurance, vd_x would

---

* The supplementary symbol $A_{x:\overline{n}|}^{1}$ is often used to denote the present value of an n year pure endowment of one dollar, since the mark "1" indicates that the benefit is payable only if the n year period expires before (x) dies, that is, only if (x) survives n years.

Except for this one instance the capital "A" with proper subscripts is invariably used to denote the present value of payments to be made upon the *death* of an individual, while the small "a" with proper subscripts is always used to represent the present value of an annuity, that is, a series of payments contingent upon the *life* of an individual.

be needed immediately to pay death claims to beneficiaries on account of deaths in the first policy year, $v^2 d_{x+1}$ would be needed to pay beneficiaries on account of deaths in the second policy, and so on, until $v^n d_{x+n-1}$ would be needed to pay beneficiaries on account of deaths in the nth year, after which all the remaining policies would expire. Hence, equating the present value of the total net premiums to the total present value of the benefit, we find

$$l_x \cdot A^1_{x:\,\overline{n}|} = v d_x + v^2 d_{x+1} + v^3 d_{x+2} + \cdots + v^n d_{x+n-1}.$$

The net single premium for each policy is found by dividing both members of this equation by l_x; thus we have

$$A^1_{x:\,\overline{n}|} = \frac{v d_x + v^2 d_{x+1} + v^3 d_{x+2} + \cdots + v^n d_{x+n-1}}{l_x}.$$

Multiplying numerator and denominator by v^x and inserting the commutation symbols, we obtain

$$A^1_{x:\,\overline{n}|} = \frac{C_x + C_{x+1} + C_{x+2} + \cdots + C_{x+n-1}}{D_x}.$$

Since

$$M_x = C_x + C_{x+1} + C_{x+2} + \cdots + C_{x+n-1} + C_{x+n} + \cdots + C_\omega$$

and

$$M_{x+n} = \qquad\qquad\qquad\qquad\qquad\qquad\quad C_{x+n} + \cdots + C_\omega,$$

we have, upon subtraction,

$$M_x - M_{x+n} = C_x + C_{x+1} + C_{x+2} + \cdots + C_{x+n-1},$$

and hence

(39) $$A^1_{x:\,\overline{n}|} = \frac{M_x - M_{x+n}}{D_x}.$$

The net single premium for a one year term insurance on the life of (x) is called the *natural premium* at age x and is denoted by c_x. Setting $n = 1$ in expression (39), we find

$$(40) \qquad c_x = A^1_{x:\overline{1}|} = \frac{M_x - M_{x+1}}{D_x} = \frac{C_x}{D_x},$$

since $C_x = M_x - M_{x+1}$.

If $_nP^1_{x:\overline{m}|}$ denotes * the net annual premium payable for n years $(n \leqq m)$ to provide an m year term insurance of one dollar, it follows that

$$_nP^1_{x:\overline{m}|} \cdot a_{x:\overline{n}|} = A^1_{x:\overline{m}|},$$

and hence

$$(41) \qquad _nP^1_{x:\overline{m}|} = \frac{A^1_{x:\overline{m}|}}{a_{x:\overline{n}|}} = \frac{M_x - M_{x+m}}{N_x - N_{x+n}}.$$

When the premium payment period coincides with the term insurance period, $m = n$, the notation $_nP^1_{x:\overline{n}|}$ is usually shortened to $P^1_{x:\overline{n}|}$; hence we have

$$(42) \qquad P^1_{x:\overline{n}|} = \frac{A^1_{x:\overline{n}|}}{a_{x:\overline{n}|}} = \frac{M_x - M_{x+n}}{N_x - N_{x+n}}.$$

Numerical values of c_x are shown in Table VI, whereas values of the single premiums $A^1_{x:\overline{n}|}$, for selected values of n, are given in Table XI. Unless otherwise stated, the phrase "net premium for an n year term insurance" will mean the net annual premium for an n payment n year term insurance as given by equation (42).

EXERCISES—LIST XVIII

1. Show that

(a) $A_x = A^1_{x:\overline{n}|} + _nE_x \cdot A^{\frac{1}{x+n:\overline{n}|}} + _{2n}E_x \cdot A^{\frac{1}{x+2n:\overline{n}|}} + \cdots,$

(b) $A_x = c_x + _1E_x\, c_{x+1} + _2E_x\, c_{x+2} + \cdots,$

and interpret each of these formulas verbally.

* For a given type of policy it should be noted that the prefix on the symbol for the annual premium denotes the number of premiums to be paid, while the subscripts on the right have the same meaning as those on the symbol for the net single premium.

2. Prove that

$$\text{(a) } c_x = vq_x = v \cdot \frac{d_x}{l_x}; \qquad \text{(b) } A^1_{x:\overline{n}|} = va_{x:\overline{n}|} - a_{x:\overline{n}|};$$

$$\text{(c) } P^1_{x:\overline{n}|} = v - \frac{a_{x:\overline{n}|}}{a_{x:\overline{n}|}}.$$

3. Compute to the nearest cent the numerical value of the net annual premium for each of the following policies issued at age 30, the amount of insurance in each case to be $1000:

(a) ten year term; (b) ten payment twenty year term; (c) fifty year term.

4. Derive by the mutual fund method the net single premium in terms of commutation symbols for a ten year term insurance policy for an amount R issued at age 45.

5. (a) Find the net single premium for a five year term policy for $1000 issued to a man aged 50. (b) Find the natural premiums for a $1000 insurance at each of the ages 50, 51, 52, 53, and 54. (c) Why is the sum of the five results in (b) not equal to the result of (a)?

25. Endowment Insurance. An endowment insurance provides for the payment of a benefit in event of the death of the insured within a certain period, called the endowment period, and also provides for the payment of an equal benefit at the end of the endowment period, provided the insured be then living. Hence, an n year endowment insurance may be considered as an n year term insurance plus an n year pure endowment.

If the net single premium for an n year endowment insurance of one dollar be denoted * by $A_{x:\overline{n}|}$, one has immediately

$$A_{x:\overline{n}|} = A^1_{x:\overline{n}|} + {}_nE_x,$$

by means of which the numerical value of $A_{x:\overline{n}|}$ can be computed from Tables XI and VII. Expressing each term of the right member by commutation symbols, we have

---

* The double subscript on the symbol $A_{x:\overline{n}|}$ indicates that the benefit is payable either (a) if (x) dies before the n year endowment period expires, or (b) if the n year period expires before (x) dies. Thus $A_{x:\overline{n}|} = A^1_{x:\overline{n}|} + A_{x:\overline{n}|}^{1}$

$$A_{x:\overline{n}|} = \frac{M_x - M_{x+n}}{D_x} + \frac{D_{x+n}}{D_x},$$

and hence

(43)
$$A_{x:\overline{n}|} = \frac{M_x - M_{x+n} + D_{x+n}}{D_x}.$$

The single premium $A_{x:\overline{n}|}$ for an endowment insurance may be also derived in a form similar to that shown in equation (35). We have by equation (33)

$$M_x = vN_x - N_{x+1} = (1 - d)N_x - (N_x - D_x),$$

and hence

$$M_x = D_x - dN_x,$$

and

$$M_{x+n} = D_{x+n} - dN_{x+n}.$$

Subtracting these two equations and adding D_{x+n} to each member of the result, we find

$$M_x - M_{x+n} + D_{x+n} = D_x - D_{x+n} - d(N_x - N_{x+n}) + D_{x+n},$$

and hence, after dividing by D_x,

$$A_{x:\overline{n}|} = \frac{D_x - d(N_x - N_{x+n})}{D_x},$$

or

(44)
$$A_{x:\overline{n}|} = 1 - da_{x:\overline{n}|}.$$

The symbol $_nP_{x:\overline{m}|}$ is used to denote the net annual premium payable for n years $(n \leqq m)$ for an m year endowment insurance of one dollar. Upon equating the present value of the net annual premiums to the net single premium for the benefit, one has

$$_nP_{x:\overline{m}|} \cdot a_{x:\overline{n}|} = A_{x:\overline{m}|},$$

or

(45)
$$_nP_{x:\overline{n}|} = \frac{A_{x:\overline{m}|}}{a_{x:\overline{n}|}} = \frac{M_x - M_{x+m} + D_{x+m}}{N_x - N_{x+n}}.$$

When the premium payment period coincides with the endowment period, $m = n$, the notation $_nP_{x:\overline{n}|}$ is usually shortened to $P_{x:\overline{n}|}$, and hence one has

$$(46) \qquad P_{x:\overline{n}|} = {}_nP_{x:\overline{n}|} = \frac{M_x - M_{x+n} + D_{x+n}}{N_x - N_{x+n}}.$$

Unless otherwise specified, the net annual premium for an endowment insurance will be considered as payable for the entire endowment period, and the word "endowment" will mean "endowment insurance," rather than "pure endowment." The net annual premium for an n year endowment insurance can be derived in a form similar to that shown for the ordinary life net annual premium in equation (37). After dividing equation (44) by $a_{x:\overline{n}|}$, one obtains

$$P_{x:\overline{n}|} = \frac{A_{x:\overline{n}|}}{a_{x:\overline{n}|}} = \frac{1}{a_{x:\overline{n}|}} - d.$$

Unless otherwise specified, it is to be assumed that annual premiums are payable for the entire endowment period.

EXERCISES—LIST XIX

1. Show that

$$A_{x:\overline{n}|} = va_{x:\overline{n}|} - a_{x:\overline{n-1}|}$$

and interpret this formula verbally.

2. Compute the net annual premium for a $1000 twenty year endowment insurance policy issued at age 20. Age 40. Age 60.

3. Compute the net annual premium at age 35 for each of the following policies (amount of insurance $1000):

    (a) ten year endowment;

    (b) ten payment endowment at age 65 (maturing at age 65);

    (c) twenty payment thirty year endowment.

4. Assuming that the gross premium is the same as the net premium, how large an endowment policy maturing in fifteen years can be purchased by an annual payment of $100 to be paid each year for ten years by an individual now aged 40?

26. Deferred Insurance. The symbol $_r|A^1_{x:\overline{n}|}$ is used to denote the net single premium for an n year term insurance of one dollar, deferred r years, that is, the present value of one dollar to be paid at the end of the year in which (x) dies, provided he dies after attaining age $x + r$ and before attaining age $x + r + n$. Obviously, this single premium may be considered as the difference between the single premium for an $(n + r)$ year term insurance and the single premium for an r year term insurance. Thus

$$_r|A^1_{x:\overline{n}|} = A^1_{x:\overline{r+n}|} - A^1_{x:\overline{r}|} = \frac{M_x - M_{x+r+n}}{D_x} - \frac{M_x - M_{x+r}}{D_x},$$

and hence

$$(47) \qquad _r|A^1_{x:\overline{n}|} = \frac{M_{x+r} - M_{x+r+n}}{D_x}.$$

Similarly, if $_r|A_x$ denotes the net single premium for a whole life insurance of one dollar deferred r years, then

$$_r|A_x = A_x - A^1_{x:\overline{r}|} = \frac{M_x}{D_x} - \frac{M_x - M_{x+r}}{D_x},$$

and hence

$$(48) \qquad _r|A_x = \frac{M_{x+r}}{D_x}.$$

Similarly, if $_r|A_{x:\overline{n}|}$ denotes the net single premium for an n year endowment of one dollar deferred r years, then

$$_r|A_{x:\overline{n}|} = A_{x:\overline{r+n}|} - A^1_{x:\overline{r}|}$$

$$= \frac{M_x - M_{x+r+n} + D_{x+r+n}}{D_x} - \frac{M_x - M_{x+r}}{D_x},$$

and hence

$$(49) \quad _r|A_{x:\overline{n}|} = \frac{M_{x+r} - M_{x+r+n} + D_{x+r+n}}{D_x}.$$

27. Accumulated Cost of Insurance. The symbol $_nk_x$ is used to denote the net single premium payable at the end of the term for an n year term insurance of one dollar. A life insurance policy, based upon the plan of paying the premium after the insurance has expired, would have no practical value for an insurance company, inasmuch as those who die in the period of n years pay no premium and the company would have difficulty in collecting premiums from those alive at the end of the term. The notion of the accumulated cost of insurance is valuable, however, in the consideration of reserves on life insurance policies and will be used extensively in the succeeding chapter.

Since the premium $_nk_x$ is payable at the end of the n years only if the insured survives the period, the present value of the premium is $_nk_x \cdot {_nE_x}$. Equating this value to the present value of the term insurance benefit, we obtain

$$_nk_x \cdot {_nE_x} = A^1_{x:\overline{n}|},$$

and hence

$$_nk_x = \frac{A^1_{x:\overline{n}|}}{_nE_x},$$

or

$$(50) \qquad _nk_x = \frac{M_x - M_{x+n}}{D_{x+n}}.$$

When $n = 1$, the notation k_x is usually used instead of $_1k_x$; hence we write

$$(51) \qquad k_x = {_1k_x} = \frac{M_x - M_{x+1}}{D_{x+1}} = \frac{C_x}{D_{x+1}}.$$

Numerical values of $_nk_x$ and k_x may be found in Tables XII and VI, respectively.

28. General Insurance Formula. In a manner similar to that of § 17 it is now possible to set up a general expression for the value, at any time, of an insurance benefit. Thus

$$(52) \qquad R \cdot \frac{M_a - M_b}{D_c},$$

represents the value at age c of an insurance benefit of \$$R$ payable at the end of the year of death of a designated individual, provided he dies after age a and before age b. Whenever the age b is beyond the limiting age of the table the second term in the numerator disappears. The difference $(b - a)$ indicates the temporary period during which the insurance is effective. By properly choosing the ages a, b, and c, the expression (52) may be adapted to reproduce the formulas for A_x, $A^1_{x:\overline{n}|}$, $_r|A^1_{x:\overline{n}|}$, $_nk_x$, k_x, and others.

EXERCISES—LIST XX

1. A certain life insurance policy issued at age 30 provides for twenty annual premiums. In event of death of the insured between ages 30 and 40 the policy pays \$1000, in event of death between ages 40 and 50 the policy pays \$2000, and in event of the death of the insured after reaching age 50 the policy pays \$3000. Find the net annual premium.

SOLUTION. Let P denote the net annual premium. Upon equating the present value of the net premiums to the present value of the benefits, one finds

$$P \cdot a_{30:\overline{20}|} = 1000 A^1_{30:\overline{10}|} + 2000_{10}|A^1_{30:\overline{10}|} + 3000_{20}|A_{30},$$

or

$$P = \frac{1000(M_{30} - M_{40}) + 2000(M_{40} - M_{50}) + 3000 M_{50}}{N_{30} - N_{50}},$$

$$= 1000 \frac{M_{30} + M_{40} + M_{50}}{N_{30} - N_{50}}.$$

Inserting the numerical values of the commutation symbols, we have, by Table III,

$$P = 1000 \cdot \frac{24,703.369}{415,140.28} = 59.51.$$

2. A certain life insurance policy issued at age 20 provides for thirty annual premiums. The benefits provided are \$1000 in event of death during the first twenty years and \$3000 in event of death thereafter. Compute the net annual premium.

3. A certain life insurance policy provides for $1000 in event of death before age 65 with a $2000 cash payment if the insured survives to age 65. Assuming the policy is issued at age 30 and provides for ten annual premiums, compute the net annual premium.

4. The so-called "modified" life policy provides for the payment of $1000 in event of the death of the insured now aged 50. The premiums payable for the first five years are exactly one-half of the ultimate premium payable for life thereafter. Compute the ultimate net premium.

5. Prove algebraically the following identities:

(a) $A_x \cdot u_x = k_x + A_{x+1}$;   (b) $A_{x:\overline{n}|}^{1} \cdot u_x = k_x + A_{x+1:\overline{n-1}|}^{1}$;

(c) $A_{x:\overline{n}|} \cdot u_x = k_x + A_{x+1:\overline{n-1}|}$.

6. Show that

(a) $A_x = (_m k_x + A_{x+m})_m E_x$;   (b) $A_{x:\overline{n}|}^{1} = (_m k_x + A_{x+m:\overline{n-m}|}^{1})_m E_x$;

(c) $A_{x:\overline{n}|} = (_m k_x + A_{x+m:\overline{n-m}|})_m E_x$.

7. Show that

(a) $c_x \cdot u_x = k_x$;   (b) $P_{x+1} = P_x + \dfrac{P_{x+1} - c_x}{a_x}$;   (c) $P_{x:\overline{n}|}^{1} = \dfrac{_n k_x}{_n u_x}$.

8. Prove the identities

(a) $_t u_x = _{t-1} u_{x+1} + \dfrac{1}{_t E_x}$;   (b) $_t k_x = _{t-1} k_{x+1} + \dfrac{c_x}{_t E_x}$.

29. Increasing Insurance.

Consider a whole life insurance policy in which the benefit increases annually so that one dollar is payable if the insured dies in the first policy year, two dollars are payable if the insured dies in the second year, three dollars are payable if the insured dies in the third year, and so on. Such a benefit may be considered as the sum of several level whole life benefits of one dollar each, the first to begin immediately, the second deferred one year, the third deferred two years, and so on. If the net single premium for such an increasing insurance benefit issued at age x is denoted by $(IA)_x$, we have

$$(IA)_x = A_x + _1|A_x + _2|A_x + \cdots + _{\omega-x}|A_x$$
$$= \frac{M_x}{D_x} + \frac{M_{x+1}}{D_x} + \frac{M_{x+2}}{D_x} + \cdots + \frac{M_\omega}{D_x},$$

and hence

$$(IA)_x = \frac{M_x + M_{x+1} + M_{x+2} + \cdots + M_\omega}{D_x}.$$

Define the commutation symbol R_x, such that

$$R_x = M_x + M_{x+1} + M_{x+2} + \cdots + M_\omega.$$

The net single premium for the increasing whole life insurance policy can now be written

$$(53) \qquad\qquad (IA)_x = \frac{R_x}{D_x}.$$

Values of the commutation symbol R_x are given in Table III.

EXERCISES—LIST XXI

1. Calculate the net single premium for an increasing whole life insurance which begins with a death benefit of \$500 in the first policy year and increases by \$100 per year, assuming the age at issue is age 30.

SOLUTION. The single premium for this increasing benefit may be written

$$A = \frac{500v \cdot d_{30} + 600v^2 \cdot d_{31} + 700v^3 d_{32} + \cdots}{l_{30}}$$

$$= \frac{500C_{30} + 600C_{31} + 700C_{32} + \cdots}{D_{30}}$$

$$= \frac{500(C_{30}+C_{31}+C_{32}+\cdots)+100(C_{31}+C_{32}+\cdots)+100(C_{32}+C_{33}+\cdots)+\cdots}{D_{30}}$$

$$= \frac{500M_{30} + 100(M_{31} + M_{32} + \cdots)}{D_{30}}$$

$$= \frac{500M_{30} + 100R_{31}}{D_{30}}.$$

Since $M_{30} = R_{30} - R_{31}$, the single premium A may be written

$$A = \frac{400M_{30} + 100R_{30}}{D_{30}}.$$

After inserting the numerical values of the commutation symbols, we find by Table III,

$$A = \frac{32,005,469}{30,440.784} = 1051.40$$

2. Show that if the term of the insurance described in § 29 be limited to n years, the net single premium becomes

$$(IA)^1_{x:\overline{n}|} = \frac{R_x - R_{x+n} - n \cdot M_{x+n}}{D_x}.$$

3. Show that the net single premium for an increasing insurance on the life of (x) is

$$\frac{hM_x + kR_{x+1}}{D_x},$$

if the death benefit in the first year is h, and the death benefit increases by k per year.

4. A certain policy issued at age 45 provides for the following schedule of amounts payable in event of death:

Year	1	2	3	4	5	6	7	8	9	thereafter
Amount	1000	1200	1400	1600	1800	2000	1500	1000	500	0

(a) Compute the net single premium for the above policy.

(b) What net annual premium payable for five years will purchase the above policy?

5. A child's endowment policy issued at age 1 provides for a death benefit of $100 in event of death the first year, $200 in event of death the second year, and so on, increasing by $100 per year until a maximum of $1000 is reached. The policy matures at age 21 with an endowment of $1000. Show that the net annual premium payable for twenty years is

$$1000 \frac{0.1(R_1 - R_{11}) - M_{21} + D_{21}}{N_1 - N_{21}}.$$

6. A certain life insurance policy provides for $10,000 payable in event of death between age x and age 41, $9700 in event of death between ages 41 and 42, $9400 in event of death between ages 42 and 43, and so on, decreasing $300 each year until the amount of insurance reaches $1000 at age 70, after which it remains constant. Premiums are payable from age x to age 64, inclusive.

(a) Show that the net annual premium for this policy may be expressed in the form

$$\frac{10,000M_x - 300(R_{41} - R_{71})}{N_x - N_{65}}.$$

(b) Compute the net annual premium for age 25 at issue.

7. Describe the type of insurance whose net single premium is given by each of the following:

(a) $\dfrac{1000}{D_x}(M_x + 3R_{x+1})$;   (b) $\dfrac{1000}{D_{25}}[M_{25} + 2(R_{30} - R_{35})]$;

(c) $\dfrac{100}{D_x}(M_x + 3R_{x+2} + 3R_{x+3})$.

8. Describe the type of policy whose net annual premium is given by each of the following:

(a) $1000\dfrac{M_x + R_{x+1}}{N_x - N_{x+10}}$;   (b) $1000\dfrac{R_x}{N_x}$;   (c) $\dfrac{1000(M_x - M_{x+1b})}{N_x}$.

(d) Would the policy whose net annual premium is given by (c) be practical for issue by a life insurance company?

9. Show that

(a) $R_x = vS_x - S_{x+1}$;   (b) $R_x = N_x - d \cdot S_x$;

(c) $a_x = (IA)_x + d \cdot (Ia)_x$.

10. A certain whole life policy provides for a death benefit in the nth year of $(1.01)^n$. Assuming that the company operates upon a three and one-half per cent interest basis, show that the net annual premium for the policy is approximately

$$\frac{A_x}{a_x},$$

in which the numerator is computed at $2\frac{1}{2}\%$ and the denominator at $3\frac{1}{2}\%$.

30. Return of Premium Policy.

Some life insurance contracts provide for the return, at the time of death of the insured, of all the net premiums which he has paid. This benefit is usually given in addition to the payment of the face amount of insurance.

Consider an ordinary life policy which provides for the payment, at the death of the insured, of the face amount \$1 together with the return, without interest, of all the net premiums paid by the insured prior to his death. Let P denote the net annual premium for this contract. In event of the death of the insured during the first policy year the company agrees to pay the face amount \$1 and return the first premium P. Hence the total amount payable in event of death in the first policy year is $(1 + P)$. In event of the death of the insured during the second policy year the company pays the face amount \$1 in addition to the return of two net premiums, which the insured paid at the beginning of the first and second policy years. Thus the total amount of insurance during the second policy year is $(1 + 2P)$. Similarly, the total amount of insurance during the third policy year is $(1 + 3P)$, the fourth policy year $(1 + 4P)$, and so on, increasing by P per year. The return of the net premiums forms an increasing insurance and, since the present value of the net premiums must equal the present value of the benefits, it follows that

$$P \cdot a_x = A_x + P \cdot (IA)_x.$$

Solving for the net premium P and inserting commutation symbols, we obtain

(54) $$P = \frac{A_x}{a_x - (IA)_x} = \frac{M_x}{N_x - R_x}.$$

EXERCISES—LIST XXII

1. A special twenty year endowment policy issued at age x provides, in event of the death of the insured during the twenty year period, for a benefit of \$1 and the return, without interest, of all net premiums paid. If the insured survives the twenty year period the policy matures, the insured receiving only the face amount \$1. Show that the net annual premium may be written in the form

$$\frac{M_x - M_{x+20} + D_{x+20}}{N_x - N_{x+20} - R_x + R_{x+20} + 20M_{x+20}}.$$

2. Express in terms of commutation symbols the net annual premium for a twenty payment life policy issued at age x which provides, in event of the death of the insured during the first twenty policy years, for the return, without interest, of all net premiums paid in addition to the face amount of \$1.

3. A single premium whole life policy issued at age x provides for the return, without interest, of the net single premium together with the payment of the face amount \$1 at the death of the insured.

(a) Express the net single premium in terms of commutation symbols.

(b) Compute the net single premium for $x = 35$.

4. A life annuity contract, issued at age 30, provides for the payment of $1000 a year, first payment at age 60. The annuity is to be purchased by annual premiums payable for thirty years. In event of the death of the policyholder prior to age 60, the net premiums already paid are to be returned, without interest. Compute the net premium.

REVIEW EXERCISE—LIST XXIII

1. What is the difference between the net annual premium for a $1000 ordinary life policy issued at age 30 and the net annual premium for a 55 year endowment issued for the same amount at the same age? (The latter policy, endowing at age 85, is frequently issued by life insurance companies in place of the ordinary life.)

2. What are the two principal reasons why an individual should not delay in purchasing his insurance?

3. Express in commutation symbols the net single premium for a whole life insurance policy which provides that the beneficiary receive $1000 at the death of the insured and $1000 per year for the subsequent nine years?

4. Draw a graph showing the values of the natural premiums for ages above 50 and indicate thereon the value of the ordinary life net annual premium for age 50.

5. A certain single premium contract provides for a pure endowment of $1000 payable if (x) survives n years. In event of the death of (x) before age $x + n$ the single premium is to be returned without interest. Express the net single premium in terms of commutation symbols.

6. Complete the following table expressing each of the symbols a_x, A_x, and P_x entirely in terms of each of the others and the discount factor d.

	a_x	A_x	P_x
a_x	a_x		
A_x	$1 - da_x$	A_x	
P_x	$\dfrac{1}{a_x} - d$		P_x

7. Complete the following table expressing each of the symbols $a_{x:\overline{n}|}$, $A_{x:\overline{n}|}$, and $P_{x:\overline{n}|}$ entirely in terms of each of the others and the discount factor d.

	$a_{x:\overline{n}|}$	$A_{x:\overline{n}|}$	$P_{x:\overline{n}|}$
$a_{x:\overline{n}|}$	$a_{x:\overline{n}|}$		
$A_{x:\overline{n}|}$	$1 - da_{x:\overline{n}|}$	$A_{x:\overline{n}|}$	
$P_{x:\overline{n}|}$	$\dfrac{1}{a_{x:\overline{n}|}} - d$		$P_{x:\overline{n}|}$

8. Express each of the following entirely in terms of whole life and temporary life annuity symbols and the rate of interest.

(a) Annual premium for 20 year term insurance.

(b) Annual premium for 20 year pure endowment.

9. Use commutation symbols to prove that

$$\frac{A_{x+n} - A_x}{1 - A_x} + \frac{a_{x+n}}{a_x} = 1.$$

10. Compute the net single premium to provide an annuity of $100 per year payable in equal installments at the beginning of each quarter for as long as (50) survives, with the condition that if death occurs in the first policy year, four-fifths of the premium will be refunded; this death benefit to decrease by one-fifth of the premium each year until it disappears.

11. A man aged x offers to pay a lump sum of $_nE_x$ and also an annual premium of $P^1_{x:\overline{n}|}$ for an endowment policy maturing at age $x + n$. Find the amount of the policy.

12. Show that:

(a) $$P^1_{x:\overline{n}|} = v - a_{x:\overline{n}|} (P_{x:\overline{n}|} + d);$$

(b) $$a_{x:\overline{n}|} = \frac{1 - A_{x:\overline{n+1}|}}{d} - 1.$$

13. Under a certain mortality table $A_x = 0.01 \cdot x$ for all values of x when the rate of interest is 4%. Find expressions for a_x and P_x.

14. A certain t year endowment policy issued at age x provides for the payment of $a_{\overline{m}|}$ in event death occurs during the first policy year, $a_{\overline{2m}|}$ in event death occurs during the second policy year, etc., and $a_{\overline{tm}|}$ in event death occurs during the tth policy year or in event (x) survives the t year period. Show that the net single premium at rate i for this policy can be expressed as

$$\frac{A_{x:\overline{t}|} - A'_{x:\overline{t}|}}{d},$$

where $A_{x:\overline{t}|}$ is calculated at rate i and $A'_{x:\overline{t}|}$ is calculated at a different rate of interest.

CHAPTER IV

NET LEVEL RESERVE

31. Reserves. All mortality tables show a rate of mortality which, except at the very low ages, is increasing from age to age. Thus, if the amount of insurance provided by a given policy is the same year after year, the current cost of the insurance benefit (as indicated by the natural premium c_x) will increase from policy year to policy year. Under these conditions the net level premium for the policy is, in the early policy years, more than sufficient to cover the current cost of the insurance, and, in the later policy years the level premium is insufficient to pay the increased cost, current in these later years. The significance of this statement may be readily understood by considering a numerical example. Under the American Experience Table, with $3\frac{1}{2}\%$ interest, the net level premium for a $1000 ordinary life policy issued at age 40 is $23.50. The cost of insurance in the first policy year is $1000c_{40}$, or $9.46 as given by Table VI. In the second policy year the net level premium is the same, $23.50, while the cost of insurance is now $1000c_{41}$, or $9.67. The cost of the insurance gradually rises from year to year, reaching $23.88 at age 59 and $139.58 at age 80, whereas the net level premium remains constant at the original amount, $23.50. The diagram shown on page 73 compares graphically the net level premium $23.50 with the increasing annual cost of the insurance benefit provided by an ordinary life policy issued at age 40.

It should be noted that at the older ages the cost of insurance greatly exceeds the net level premium. If the insurance company is to continue upon a solvent basis, it is necessary that the company accumulate a fund from the excess of the net level premium over the current cost during the early policy years in order to be able to provide for the increased cost in the later policy years. The accumulation of this "excess" is called the *reserve*.

GRAPHICAL COMPARISON OF NET LEVEL PREMIUM
For Ordinary Life with One-Year Premiums
Age at Issue 40   American Experience 3½%

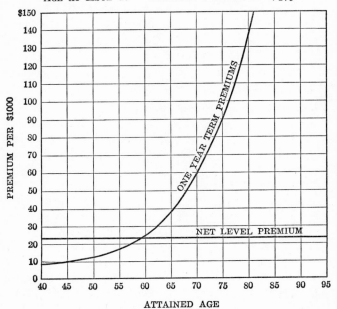

The necessity of accumulating reserves may also be seen from another point of view. When a policy is issued, the net level premium is so calculated as to make the present value of the net premiums exactly equal to the present value of the benefits. This equation holds only at the date of issue of the policy. At any time thereafter the present value of the remaining net premiums is less than upon the date of issue since a fewer number of premiums remain to be received, while the present value of the insurance has increased because the date of payment has drawn nearer. The difference between the increased value of the insurance benefits and the decreased value of the future net premiums must be represented by funds which the company has on hand in its reserve fund.

The first point of view deals exclusively with the past history of the policy and is "retrospective," while the second point of view is concerned with the future of the policy and is "prospective." It is natural to suppose that these two methods will give identical amounts of reserve; this equality will be shown later.

32. Numerical Illustration. Suppose that a life insurance company issues a three payment six year endowment policy for an amount of \$1 to each of l_{40} individuals at age 40. Assume that the company has available, after expenses have been met, a net level premium from each policy based upon the American Experience $3\frac{1}{2}\%$ table. Under this assumption the company would have

$$_3P_{40:\overline{6}|} = \frac{M_{40} - M_{46} + D_{46}}{N_{40} - N_{43}} = 0.2848216$$

available from each policy to meet the current costs of insurance and maintain the reserve fund. At the beginning of the first year l_{40}, or 78,106, premiums of 0.2848216 are collected, producing an initial fund of \$22,246.28. At the end of the year interest at $3\frac{1}{2}\%$ is added, giving a total of \$23,024.90. At the end of the year d_{40}, or 765, death claims of \$1 each are paid, leaving a balance of \$22,259.90. There are $l_{41} = 77,341$ survivors, so that the total fund \$22,259.90, divided by 77,341, gives \$0.28782 as the share, or reserve, per policy. At the beginning of the second year \$22,028.39

in premiums is collected from 77,341 policyholders, and this amount is added to the balance remaining from the previous year, and so on. The table below shows the result of the numerical calculations:

Year	Total Premiums Received	Total Fund at Beginning of Year	Fund with Interest	Death Claims	Fund at End of Year	Number of Survivors	Reserve per Policy
1	$22,246.28	$22,246.28	$23,024.90	765	$22,259.90	77,341	0.28782
2	22,028.39	44,288.29	45,838.38	774	45,064.38	76,567	0.58856
3	21,807.94	66,872.32	69,212.85	785	68,427.85	75,782	0.90296
4	—	68,427.85	70,822.82	797	70,025.82	74,985	0.93386
5	—	70,025.82	72,476.72	812	71,664.72	74,173	0.96618
6	—	71,664.72	74,172.99	828	73,344.99	73,345	1.00000

It should be noted that in accordance with the provisions of the policy no premiums are collected after the third year, and that the reserve at the end of the sixth year is just sufficient to provide the endowment payment of $1 at that time.

The reserves, as exhibited in the table, are those which are on hand at the end of the various policy years and are known as *terminal reserves*. Thus, the figure, 0.58856, appearing in the last column of the second line, is called the second terminal reserve, and represents the amount on hand for each policy remaining in force at the end of the second policy year just before the third premium is paid. In the formation of the table it was tacitly assumed that all of the living policyholders continue their policies by paying premiums as they come due. In a practical situation, some of the living policyholders may fail to pay one or more premiums, and in this event the terminal reserve would furnish a criterion as to the company's liability to the policyholder.

EXERCISES—LIST XXIV

1. Make a table similar in form to that of § 32, showing the accumulation of the reserves for a five year endowment policy issued at age 50 on the A.E. $3\frac{1}{2}\%$ basis.

2. Make a table similar in form to that of § 32, showing the accumulation of the reserves for a five year term policy issued at age 20 on the A.E. $3\frac{1}{2}\%$ basis.

33. Retrospective Reserve.
The method given by the table in § 32 is too long and cumbersome to be of much practical use in the calculation of terminal reserves. Attention will now be given to more convenient methods. From the retrospective point of view the terminal reserve for a given policy is defined as the difference between the accumulated value of past net premiums and the accumulated value of past insurance benefits. Hence, for a policy issued at age x, the tth terminal reserve represents this difference at the end of the tth policy year, when the insured attains age $x + t$, so that

$$\begin{pmatrix} t\text{th Terminal} \\ \text{reserve} \end{pmatrix} = \begin{pmatrix} \text{Accumulated value at} \\ \text{age } x + t \text{ of} \\ \text{past net premiums} \end{pmatrix}$$
$$- \begin{pmatrix} \text{Accumulated value at} \\ \text{age } x + t \text{ of past} \\ \text{insurance benefits} \end{pmatrix}.$$

Let us apply this definition to obtain an expression for the tth terminal reserve for an ordinary life policy issued at age x. By the end of the t year period following the date of issue the company has received t premiums of P_x each, paid at the beginning of each year throughout this period. The accumulated value at age $x + t$ of these net premiums is $P_x \cdot {}_t u_x$. The accumulated cost of the insurance in force over the temporary period of t years is $\$1 \cdot {}_t k_x$. Denoting the tth terminal reserve for a $\$1$ ordinary life policy issued at age x by the symbol ${}_t V_x$, we have

(55) $\qquad {}_t V_x = P_x \cdot {}_t u_x - {}_t k_x,$

and, referring to §§ 16 and 27, we obtain

$${}_t V_x = \frac{1}{D_{x+t}} [P_x(N_x - N_{x+t}) - (M_x - M_{x+t})].$$

Similarly, if the tth terminal reserve for an n payment life be denoted by $_{t:n}V_x$, then if $t \leqq n$, we find

(56) $$_{t:n}V_x = {}_nP_x \cdot {}_tu_x - {}_tk_x.$$

In considering the tth terminal reserve for an n payment life policy with $t > n$, it should be noted that no premiums are paid for the interval of time elapsing from the end of the nth policy year to the end of the tth policy year. The accumulated value of past net premiums is $_nP_x \cdot {}_nu_x$ at the end of the premium payment period, and this amount is then accumulated, with the benefit of interest and survivorship, to the end of the tth policy year. The accumulation factor for this latter interval is

$$\frac{1}{_{t-n}E_{x+n}},$$

since $x + n$ is the age attained by the insured at the beginning of the interval and $(t - n)$ is the number of years for which this accumulation is to be made. Thus, for values of $t > n$, the retrospective formula becomes

(57) $$_{t:n}V_x = \frac{_nP_x \cdot {}_nu_x}{_{t-n}E_{x+n}} - {}_tk_x = \frac{1}{D_{x+t}}[_nP_x(N_x - N_{x+n}) - (M_x - M_{x+t})].$$

Similarly, for an n year endowment * of \$1 issued at age x, the retrospective method yields

(58) $$_tV_{x:\overline{n}|} = P_{x:\overline{n}|} \cdot {}_tu_x - {}_tk_x = \frac{1}{D_{x+t}}[P_{x:\overline{n}|}(N_x - N_{x+t}) - (M_x - M_{x+t})].$$

EXERCISES—LIST XXV

1. Compute by the retrospective method the third terminal reserve for the three payment six year endowment policy of § 32.

* It should be noted that the first subscript in the symbol for the terminal reserve for a given policy indicates the policy year at the end of which the reserve is to be taken, while the other subscripts have the same meaning as the subscripts in the symbol for the net annual premium.

SOLUTION. Applying the retrospective definition of the third terminal reserve, we obtain immediately

$$_{3:3}V_{40:\overline{5}|} = (_3P_{40:\overline{5}|})(_3u_{40}) - _3k_{40}.$$

Using Tables X and XII, we find

$$_{3:3}V_{40:\overline{5}|} = (0.2848216)(3.281702) - 0.03174338 = 0.902956,$$

which checks with the numerical value found in § 32.

2. By the retrospective method obtain a simple form for the nth terminal reserve for each of the following policies: (a) an n year term insurance policy; (b) an n payment life policy; (c) an n year endowment policy.

3. Express in terms of commutation symbols the 25th terminal reserve for a twenty payment thirty year endowment policy issued at age 35. Show that this expression is equal to $A_{60:\overline{5}|}$.

4. Find numerical values for the fifth terminal reserves for the following $1000 policies issued at age 25: (a) ordinary life; (b) twenty payment life; (c) twenty year endowment; (d) ten year term.

5. Find numerical values for the tenth terminal reserves for the following policies issued at age 25: (a) ordinary life; (b) twenty payment life; (c) twenty year endowment; (d) five payment life.

6. Compute the fifteenth terminal reserve for each of the following $1000 policies issued at age 40: (a) ten payment life; (b) ten payment twenty year endowment; (c) twenty payment thirty year endowment.

34. Prospective Reserve. From the prospective point of view the terminal reserve for a given policy is defined as the difference between the value of the future benefits of the policy and the value of the future net premiums. Hence, for a policy issued at age x, the tth terminal reserve represents this difference in values at the end of the tth policy year, when the insured attains age $x + t$, so that

$$\begin{pmatrix} \text{Prospective} \\ \text{reserve} \end{pmatrix} = \begin{pmatrix} \text{Value at age } x + t \\ \text{of} \\ \text{future benefits} \end{pmatrix} - \begin{pmatrix} \text{Value at age } x + t \\ \text{of} \\ \text{future net premiums} \end{pmatrix}.$$

Consider an ordinary life policy issued at age x for a face amount of insurance of one dollar. At the end of the tth policy year, the future premiums constitute a life annuity due of P_x, payable at the beginning of each year for the lifetime of an individual age $x + t$. Since the value of these future premiums is $P_x \cdot a_{x+t}$ and the value of the future benefits to be provided by the ordinary life policy is A_{x+t}, the prospective method gives

$$(59) \qquad {}_t V_x = A_{x+t} - P_x \cdot a_{x+t},$$

or

$$ {}_t V_x = \frac{1}{D_{x+t}} [M_{x+t} - P_x \cdot N_{x+t}]. $$

Similarly, for the tth terminal reserve upon a one dollar n payment life policy issued at age x, $t \leqq n$, we have

$$(60) \qquad {}_{t:n} V_x = A_{x+t} - {}_n P_x \cdot a_{x+t:\overline{n-t}|},$$

since the future premiums constitute in this case a temporary life annuity for $(n - t)$ years, which is the balance of the premium payment period. When the terminal reserve is required at the end of a policy year subsequent to the end of the premium payment period, $t > n$, the value of the future premiums is zero; consequently we have

$$ {}_{t:n} V_x = A_{x+t}. $$

In considering the tth terminal reserve for a one dollar n year endowment policy, the future benefits consist of endowment insurance for $(n - t)$ years, while the future premiums constitute a temporary annuity due payable for $(n - t)$ years. Applying the prospective definition for the reserve, we have

$$(61) \qquad {}_t V_{x:\overline{n}|} = A_{x+t:\overline{n-t}|} - P_{x:\overline{n}|} \cdot a_{x+t:\overline{n-t}|},$$

and hence

$$ {}_t V_{x:\overline{n}|} = \frac{1}{D_{x+t}} [M_{x+t} - M_{x+n} + D_{x+n} - P_{x:\overline{n}|}(N_{x+t} - N_{x+n})]. $$

It will be shown in the next section that the two definitions, retrospective and prospective, for the terminal reserve are equivalent.

EXERCISES—LIST XXVI

1. Compute by the prospective method the first terminal reserve for the three payment six year endowment policy of § 32.

SOLUTION. Upon applying the prospective definition of the first terminal reserve, we obtain immediately

$$_{1:3}V_{40:\overline{6}|} = A_{41:\overline{5}|} - {}_3P_{40:\overline{6}|} \cdot a_{41:\overline{2}|}.$$

Using Tables VII, XI, and IX, we find
$$_{1:3}V_{40:\overline{6}|} = .04660200 + .7984707 - (0.2848216)(1.956514)$$
$$= 0.2878153,$$

which checks with the numerical value found in § 32.

2. Find the numerical values for the fifth terminal reserve by the prospective method for the following $1000 policies issued at age 25: (a) ordinary life; (b) twenty payment life; (c) twenty year endowment; (d) ten year term.

3. Express in terms of commutation symbols the 25th terminal reserve for a twenty payment thirty year endowment policy issued at age x.

4. Compute the tenth terminal reserve by the prospective method for a $1000 twenty payment endowment insurance maturing at age 65, the policy having been issued at age 35.

5. Compute by the prospective method the fifteenth terminal reserve for each of the following $1000 policies issued at age 25: (a) ordinary life; (b) ten payment life; (c) ten payment twenty year endowment; (d) thirty year endowment.

6. Show algebraically that the retrospective and prospective methods give identical values for the tth terminal reserve for an ordinary life policy issued at age x.

7. Same as problem (6) for a twenty payment life policy, (a) for $t \leqq 20$, (b) for $t > 20$.

35. Equivalence of the Retrospective and Prospective Definitions.
In order to show that the retrospective and prospective methods of obtaining a given reserve always

produce identical results consider the fundamental equation used in determining the net premium, namely,

$$\begin{pmatrix}\text{Value at age of issue} \\ \text{of all net premiums}\end{pmatrix} = \begin{pmatrix}\text{Value at age of issue} \\ \text{of all policy benefits}\end{pmatrix}.$$

Accumulating both sides of this equation with the benefit of interest and survivorship to the date at which the reserve is to be taken, we have

$$\begin{pmatrix}\text{Value at reserve date} \\ \text{of all net premiums}\end{pmatrix} = \begin{pmatrix}\text{Value at reserve date} \\ \text{of all policy benefits}\end{pmatrix}.$$

The value of all net premiums at the reserve date may be separated into two parts, (a) the accumulated value of all net premiums paid before the reserve date, and (b) the value of all future premiums. Similarly, the value of all policy benefits at the reserve date may be divided into two parts, (a) the accumulated value of the temporary insurance provided by the policy prior to the reserve date, and (b) the value of all future policy benefits. Hence, it follows that (all values refer to the reserve date)

$$\begin{pmatrix}\text{Accumulated value} \\ \text{of past premiums}\end{pmatrix} + \begin{pmatrix}\text{Value of} \\ \text{future premiums}\end{pmatrix}$$

$$= \begin{pmatrix}\text{Accumulated value} \\ \text{of past benefits}\end{pmatrix} + \begin{pmatrix}\text{Value of} \\ \text{future benefits}\end{pmatrix}.$$

Transposing the second term and the third term of this equation, we obtain immediately

$$\begin{pmatrix}\text{Retrospective} \\ \text{reserve}\end{pmatrix} = \begin{pmatrix}\text{Prospective} \\ \text{reserve}\end{pmatrix}.$$

EXERCISES—LIST XXVII

1. A twenty payment insurance policy provides for the following death benefits:

$1000 in event of death during the first five years;
$2000 in event of death during the next five years; and
$3000 in event of death thereafter.

Give in terms of commutation symbols formulas for:

(a) the net annual premium;

(b) the 7th terminal reserve by the retrospective method;

(c) the 7th terminal reserve by the prospective method;

(d) Show that the expressions found under (b) and (c) are equal.

SOLUTION. (a) Equating the present value of the net premiums to the present value of the benefits, we obtain

$$P \cdot a_{x:\overline{20}|} = 1000A_x + 1000_5|A_x + 1000_{10}|A_x.$$

Inserting commutation symbols and solving for P, we have

$$P = \frac{1000(M_x + M_{x+5} + M_{x+10})}{N_x - N_{x+20}}.$$

(b) In considering the accumulated cost of insurance under this policy at the end of the 7th year, one must bear in mind that the insurance benefit increased at the end of the 5th year from \$1000 to \$2000. By the end of the 7th year, the insured has had the benefit of \$1000 insurance for 7 years and an additional \$1000 for the last two years. Hence the accumulated cost of insurance is $1000(_7k_x + {}_2k_{x+5})$. Applying the retrospective definition of the 7th reserve, we obtain

$$_7V = P \cdot {}_7u_x - 1000(_7k_x + {}_2k_{x+5})$$

$$= P \frac{N_x - N_{x+7}}{D_{x+7}} - 1000 \frac{M_x + M_{x+5} - 2M_{x+7}}{D_{x+7}}.$$

(c) The future benefits of this policy, valued at the end of 7 years, consist of a whole life insurance of \$2000 and an additional \$1000 whole life insurance deferred 3 years. Hence, applying the prospective definition, we find

$$_7V = 2000A_{x+7} + 1000_3|A_{x+7} - P \cdot a_{x+7:\overline{13}|}$$

$$= 1000 \frac{2M_{x+7} + M_{x+10}}{D_{x+7}} - P \frac{N_{x+7} - N_{x+20}}{D_{x+7}}.$$

(d) The following method of proving that the 7th terminal reserves found by the prospective and retrospective methods are identical is patterned after § 35. From (a), we have

$$\frac{P}{D_x}(N_x - N_{x+20}) = \frac{1000}{D_x}(M_x + M_{x+5} + M_{x+10}).$$

Multiplying both sides of this equation by D_x/D_{x+7} and transposing, we find

$$\frac{P}{D_{x+7}}N_x - 1000 \frac{M_x + M_{x+5}}{D_{x+7}} = \frac{1000M_{x+10}}{D_{x+7}} + P \frac{N_{x+20}}{D_{x+7}}.$$

Subtracting the expression

$$\frac{P \cdot N_{x+7} - 2000M_{x+7}}{D_{x+7}}$$

from both members of the preceding equation, we have

$$P\frac{N_x - N_{x+7}}{D_{x+7}} - 1000\frac{M_x + M_{x+5} - 2M_{x+7}}{D_{x+7}}$$
$$= 1000\frac{2M_{x+7} + M_{x+10}}{D_{x+7}} - P\frac{N_{x+7} - N_{x+20}}{D_{x+7}},$$

or

7th retrospective reserve = 7th prospective reserve.

2. (a) Give in terms of commutation symbols the prospective formula for the 23rd terminal reserve on a ten payment twenty-five year endowment issued at age x.

(b) Give in terms of commutation symbols the retrospective formula for the same reserve.

(c) Prove algebraically that the formulas found in (a) and (b) are equivalent.

3. A certain life insurance policy provides for \$100 payable in event of death the first year, \$200 payable in event of death the second year, \$300 payable in event of death the third year, and so on. Level premiums are payable for life. Assuming that the policy is issued at age 30, compute (a) the net annual premium, (b) the 10th terminal reserve by the prospective method, and (c) the 10th terminal reserve by the retrospective method.

4. A certain life insurance policy provides for \$10,000 payable in event of death between age 30 and age 41, \$9700 in event of death between ages 41 and 42, \$9400 in event of death between ages 42 and 43, and so on, decreasing \$300 each year until the amount of insurance reaches \$1000 at age 70, after which it remains constant. The policy is issued at age 30, and provides for annual premiums for thirty-five years. Compute the twentieth terminal reserve

(a) by the prospective method,

(b) by the retrospective method.

(See Exercise 6, List XXI.)

36. Other Formulas. It is evident that the terminal reserve for a given policy may be expressed in many different forms. Some of these forms are interesting because they afford verbal interpretations, others because of their adaptability in computing. As an illustration, replacing in formula (59) the symbol A_{x+t} by $P_{x+t} \cdot a_{x+t}$, we obtain

$$_tV_x = (P_{x+t} - P_x) \cdot a_{x+t}.$$

A verbal interpretation of this form is as follows: An ordinary life insurance policy issued at age x provides for a premium payment annually of P_x. If, after reaching age $x + t$, the insured desires to duplicate the benefits afforded by this policy, he must purchase a new ordinary life policy issued at age $x + t$ and providing for annual premiums of P_{x+t}. Thus, the deficit in future premiums, which must be made up by the reserve, is $(P_{x+t} - P_x)a_{x+t}$.

Making use of the identities

$$A_x = 1 - d \cdot a_x, \qquad P_x + d = \frac{1}{a_x},$$

we may write formula (59) in the form

(62) $$_tV_x = 1 - \frac{a_{x+t}}{a_x}.$$

This form is particularly useful in the computation of reserves and will be discussed further in a later section.

EXERCISES—LIST XXVIII

1. Show that the tth terminal reserve for an ordinary life policy issued at age x can be written in each of the following forms.

(a) $\dfrac{A_{x+t} - A_x}{1 - A_x}$.

(b) $1 - \dfrac{1 - A_{x+t}}{1 - A_x}$.

(c) $\dfrac{a_x - a_{x+t}}{1 + a_x}$.

(d) $A_{x+t}\left(1 - \dfrac{P_x}{P_{x+t}}\right)$.

2. Given that $a_x + a_{x+2t} = 2a_{x+t}$, find $_tV_{x+t}$ and $_{2t}V_x$ in terms of $_tV_x$.

3. If $1 - A_{x+2t} = A_{x+2t} - A_{x+t} = A_{x+t} - A_x$, express $_tV_{x+t}$ in terms of $_tV_x$ and find the numerical values of $_tV_{x+t}$ and $_tV_x$.

4. Prove the identity

$$_{t+r}V_x = 1 - (1 - {}_rV_x)(1 - {}_tV_{x+r}).$$

5. Employ the result of Exercise 4 to prove that
$$_tV_x = 1 - (1 - {}_1V_x)(1 - {}_1V_{x+1}) \cdots (1 - {}_1V_{x+t-1}).$$

6. Show that the tth terminal reserve for an n year endowment policy can be written in each of the following forms:

(a) $\dfrac{A_{x+t:\overline{n-t}|} - A_{x:\overline{n}|}}{1 - A_{x:\overline{n}|}}.$

(c) $(P_{x+t:\overline{n-t}|} - P_{x:\overline{n}|})a_{x+t:\overline{n-t}|}.$

(b) $1 - \dfrac{a_{x+t:\overline{n-t}|}}{a_{x:\overline{n}|}}.$

(d) $A_{x+t:\overline{n-t}|}\left(1 - \dfrac{P_{x:\overline{n}|}}{P_{x+t:\overline{n-t}|}}\right).$

7. Show that the tth terminal reserve for an n payment life policy issued at age x can be written, for $t \leqq n$, in the form
$$_{t:n}V_x = (_{n-t}P_{x+t} - {}_nP_x)a_{x+t:\overline{n-t}|},$$
and give a verbal interpretation of this form.

8. Show that the tth terminal reserve for an n year term policy issued at age x can be written in the form
$$_tV_{x:\overline{n}|}^1 = (P\frac{1}{x+t:\overline{n-t}|} - P_{x:\overline{n}|}^1)a_{x+t:\overline{n-t}|},$$
and give a verbal interpretation of this form.

37. Fackler's Accumulation Formula. A useful formula for obtaining sequentially the reserves upon a given policy may be derived by simplifying the method used in building the table shown in § 32. Explicit notation is omitted in the derivation, since the method is entirely general and the formula may be used for any policy. Consider a life insurance company issuing the same policy in amount of one dollar to each of l_x persons at age x. After t years the total reserve fund held by the company for the survivors of this group is $l_{x+t} \cdot {}_tV$. The net premiums collected by the company at the beginning of the succeeding year total $l_{x+t} \cdot P$. During this succeeding year interest at the assumed rate i is earned and at the end of the year d_{x+t} death claims of one dollar each are payable. The balance left at the end of the year represents the total reserve fund held for the l_{x+t+1} policyholders who survive this year, or $l_{x+t+1} \cdot {}_{t+1}V$. From the preceding argument it follows that

(63) $\quad (l_{x+t} \cdot {}_tV + l_{x+t} \cdot P)(1 + i) - d_{x+t} = l_{x+t+1} \cdot {}_{t+1}V.$

Dividing this equation by l_{x+t+1} and multiplying the numerator and denominator of each term of the first member by v^{x+t+1}, we have

$$(_tV + P)\frac{D_{x+t}}{D_{x+t+1}} - \frac{C_{x+t}}{D_{x+t+1}} = {}_{t+1}V,$$

and hence

(64) $$(_tV + P)\, u_{x+t} - k_{x+t} = {}_{t+1}V.$$

Equation (64), known as *Fackler's Accumulation Formula*, affords an effective means of calculating sequentially the respective terminal reserves on a policy. For $t = 0$, since $_0V = 0$, equation (64) becomes

(65) $$P \cdot u_x - k_x = {}_1V,$$

and for $t = 1$,

(66) $$(_1V + P)\, u_{x+1} - k_{x+1} = {}_2V,$$

and so on. In applying the formula the first terminal reserve is computed by means of (65) and the result inserted in equation (66) to obtain the second reserve, and so on. For policy years after the expiration of the premium payment period the net premium is omitted from the formula.

EXERCISES—LIST XXIX

1. Use Fackler's Accumulation Formula to compute the first five terminal reserves for a $1000 ten year endowment policy issued at age 25. Check the 5th terminal reserve by means of the prospective method.

SOLUTION. Employing formula (45) with $m = n = 10$, we have

$$P = \frac{1000A_{25:\,\overline{10|}}}{a_{25:\,\overline{10|}}} = \frac{1000A^1_{25:\,\overline{10|}} + 1000{}_{10}E_{25}}{a_{25:\,\overline{10|}}}.$$

The values of $1000A^1_{25:\,\overline{10|}}$, $1000{}_{10}E_{25}$, and $a_{25:\,\overline{10|}}$ are found in Tables XI, VII, and IX, respectively; hence we have immediately

$$P = \frac{67.3198 + 651.5091}{8.314633} = 86.4535-.$$

Equation (65) gives
$$_1V = Pu_{25} - 1000k_{25},$$
and, employing Table VI, we find
$$_1V = (86.4535)(1.0434146) - 8.13008 = 82.0768.$$
Using equation (66) to compute the second terminal reserve, we obtain
$$_2V = (_1V + P)u_{26} - 1000k_{26}$$
$$= (82.0768 + 86.4535)(1.0434836) - 8.19672 = 167.6619.$$
Similarly, we find
$$_3V = (167.6619 + 86.4535)(1.0435537) - 8.26446 = 256.9186,$$
$$_4V = (256.9186 + 86.4535)(1.0436250) - 8.33333 = 350.0184,$$
and, finally,
$$_5V = (350.0184 + 86.4535)(1.0437097) - 8.41516 = 447.1348.$$
As a check, by the prospective method, there results
$$_5V = 1000A^1_{30:\overline{5}|} + 1000_5E_{30} - Pa_{30:\overline{5}|}$$
$$= 38.2402 + 806.3100 - (86.4535)(4.596873)$$
$$= 447.1344.$$

2. Show that Fackler's Accumulation Formula can be written in the form
$$_{t+1}V = (_tV + P - c_{x+t})u_{x+t}.$$

3. Verify the six terminal reserves shown in the table in § 32 by a computation employing Fackler's Accumulation Formula.

4. Use Fackler's Accumulation Formula to compute the first ten terminal reserves for a \$1000 ordinary life policy issued at age 20.

5. Use Fackler's Accumulation Formula to compute the ten terminal reserves for a \$1000 ten year term policy issued at age 30.

6. (a) Develop by the method of § 37 the equation
$$_{r+t}V = {_tV} \cdot \frac{1}{_rE_{x+t}} + P_ru_{x+t} - {_rk_{x+t}}.$$

(b) Given that the fifth terminal reserve for a \$1000 ordinary life policy issued at age 30 is \$50.58 and the net premium is \$17.19, use the equation in (a) to compute the 15th terminal reserve for the same policy.

38. Initial Reserve, Net Amount at Risk. The *initial* reserve for a given policy is defined as the reserve at the beginning of a policy year just after the premium has been received. Thus, the initial reserve at the beginning of the tth policy year is the terminal reserve at the end of the previous year increased by the net premium paid at the beginning of the tth year. Hence, if the tth initial reserve on a given policy issued at age x be denoted by $_tI$, we have

$$_tI = _{t-1}V + P.$$

Explicit notation denoting the type of policy has been omitted from this equation, since it is valid for all plans of insurance. It should be noted that, after the premium payment period has expired, no further premiums are received and the initial reserve for any year is the terminal reserve for the previous year.

The *net amount at risk* for a given policy in the tth policy year is defined as the difference between the face amount of insurance provided in event of the death of the insured and the terminal reserve at the end of that year. If the policy provides for a payment of one dollar in event of death in the tth year, the net amount at risk in this policy year is

$$1 - _tV.$$

Equation (63) of the previous section may be reduced to an interesting relationship connecting the initial and terminal reserves and the net amount at risk. Dividing equation (63) by l_{x+t}, we obtain

$$(_tV + P)(1 + i) - \frac{d_{x+t}}{l_{x+t}} = \frac{l_{x+t+1}}{l_{x+t}} \cdot _{t+1}V;$$

hence

$$(_tV + P)(1 + i) - q_{x+t} = p_{x+t} \cdot _{t+1}V = (1 - q_{x+t})_{t+1}V.$$

Transposing the term $q_{x+t} \cdot _{t+1}V$, we find

$$(67) \qquad (_tV + P)(1 + i) - q_{x+t}(1 - _{t+1}V) = _{t+1}V.$$

The term $q_{x+t}(1 - _{t+1}V)$ is called the "cost of insurance based upon the net amount at risk." A verbal interpretation of equation (67) shows that the terminal reserve at the end of a given year consists of the difference between the initial reserve, accumulated with interest, and the cost of insurance based upon the net amount at risk.

After equation (67) is solved for the net premium P, we have

$$(68) \qquad P = vq_{x+t}\,(1 - {}_{t+1}V) + (v \cdot {}_{t+1}V - {}_{t}V).$$

Equation (68) implies that the net premium P for any policy must be sufficient to cover (a) the cost of insurance based upon the net amount at risk, and (b) the difference in the values of the two terminal reserves discounted to the beginning of the year. For most policies the quantity (a) decreases as t increases, whereas the second quantity (b) increases. The net premium, however, is constant from year to year. Thus, any endowment policy may be considered, upon applying equation (68), as consisting of two parts: (a) a term policy upon which the amount of insurance varies from year to year, being always equal to the net amount at risk for the endowment policy, and (b) a savings fund invested at rate i into which the balance of the net premium, not needed to purchase the term policy described in (a), is invested at the beginning of each year.

EXERCISES—LIST XXX

1. An individual aged 20, whose health is impaired, purchases a $1000 ordinary life policy by the payment of annual premiums which are $5.00 greater than the normal premium for that age. (a) If the usual $3\frac{1}{2}\%$ American Experience reserves are maintained by the company, for what rate of mortality does this total premium provide in the first policy year? (b) In the fifth policy year? (Use the table of reserves given in § 41.)

SOLUTION. (a) From § 41 we have immediately
$$1000 \cdot P_{20} = 13.48, \qquad 1000 \cdot {}_{1}V_{20} = 6.19.$$
Dividing each of these figures by 1000 to give the premium and reserve upon a $1 policy, we find
$$P_{20} = 0.01348. \qquad\qquad {}_{1}V_{20} = 0.00619.$$

Inasmuch as the individual is paying a premium of $5.00 per 1000 greater than the normal premium, the total net premium on a $1 policy is

$$P'_{20} = 0.01848.$$

Solving equation (67) for the rate of mortality q_{x+t}, we obtain

$$q_{x+t} = \frac{({}_tV + P)(1 + i) - {}_{t+1}V}{1 - {}_{t+1}V}.$$

Inserting the numerical values in this equation with $t = 0$, we obtain

$$q'_{20} = \frac{(0 + 0.01848)(1.035) - 0.00619}{1 - 0.00619} = 0.01302.$$

(b) Similarly, for the fifth policy year, with $t = 4$, we may write

$$q'_{24} = \frac{(0.02611 + 0.01848)(1.035) - 0.03323}{1 - 0.03323} = 0.01336.$$

2. For a twenty year endowment policy issued at age 25, compute:

(a) the first, second, and third terminal reserves;

(b) the net amount at risk in each of the first three years;

(c) the cost of insurance based upon the net amount at risk for each of these years, and verify equation (67) for $t = 0$, 1, and 2.

3. The sixteenth terminal reserve on an ordinary life policy issued at age 25 for a face amount of $1 is 0.17367. If the net premium is 0.01611, the rate of mortality in the seventeenth year 0.01001, and the interest rate 3%, find the seventeenth terminal reserve.

4. In some old records you find the net premium and the terminal reserves for the first twenty policy years on a $1000 policy issued at age 20. If the rate of interest is known to be 3%, how much of the mortality table could you reproduce and what would be your method?

5. On a 4% table the tenth and eleventh terminal reserves for a $1000 twenty year endowment policy issued at age 35 are $384.69 and $433.64, respectively. If the rate of mortality at age 45 is 0.01116, find the net premium for the policy.

6. Show that

$$P + d \cdot {}_tV = v \cdot q_{x+t}(1 - {}_tV) + v \cdot p_{x+t}({}_{t+1}V - {}_tV),$$

and give a verbal interpretation of this equation.

39. Changes in the Interest Rate. It will be observed from the following tables that an increase in the rate of interest produces a decrease in the net premium and the reserve. Thus, a life insurance company, which operates upon the basis of an interest rate of 3%, maintains a larger reserve than a company operating upon a 3½% or 4% interest basis. One also notes from the tables that the relative variation in premiums, resulting from a change in the interest rate, is larger at younger ages than at older ages.

NET LEVEL PREMIUMS

AMERICAN EXPERIENCE

$1000

	3%	3½%	4%
Ordinary life age 20	$14.41	$13.48	$12.67
Ordinary life age 40	24.75	23.50	22.35
Ordinary life age 60	58.27	56.83	55.45
Twenty payment life age 20	23.13	20.72	18.73
Twenty payment life age 40	33.14	30.75	28.63
Twenty payment life age 60	61.62	59.85	58.18
Twenty year endowment age 20	40.77	38.90	37.12
Twenty year endowment age 40	43.01	41.18	39.42
Twenty year endowment age 60	63.29	61.65	60.07

The percentage change in the reserve due to a change in the rate of interest is found to be greater for the earlier policy years. The table below shows the net level reserves on an ordinary life policy issued at age 25 for $1000 on the American Experience Table.

YEARS IN FORCE	3%	3½%	4%
5	$ 45.76	$ 40.91	$ 36.59
10	98.94	89.42	80.82
20	230.50	213.04	196.87
30	394.11	372.38	351.75
40	570.12	549.00	528.49
50	728.07	711.36	694.83
60	859.44	849.23	838.96
70	954.76	951.08	947.33

40. Calculating Machines. A modern calculating machine is constructed to add and to subtract, and by means of continued addition or subtraction it can perform multiplication and division with great rapidity. Most machines have a keyboard, on which numbers can be registered, and a sliding carriage containing two dials, one above the other. In finding the product $K \times L$, one of the factors K is registered on the keyboard, the motive crank at the side is turned until the other factor L appears on the upper dial, and then the product $K \times L$ is read from the lower dial.

A great advantage of the calculating machine lies in its ability to multiply two numbers together, and add the product to a third number, without requiring a tabulation of the intermediate steps. Thus, if it is desired to find the value of $J + K \cdot L$, the number J is first placed on the lower dial, and then the operation proceeds as in finding the product of $K \times L$. The effect will be that the product $K \cdot L$ is added to J, and the final result is read from the lower dial, giving $J + K \cdot L$, as desired. This property of the machine is particularly useful in a series of calculations where J and K are constant and L is varied. For example, if it be proposed to calculate the successive values of $10 + 5 \cdot L$ for $L = 2$, 6, 10, 15, etc., the number $J = 10$ is first placed on the lower dial, then the number $K = 5$ is punched on the keyboard, and upon turning the crank twice to register the first value of $L = 2$ on the upper dial, the result $10 + 5 \times 2$ can be read from the lower dial. Without clearing the machine the crank can now be turned four more times to rebuild the value of L (as shown on the upper dial) to the second number (6) and now the new value of the result appears in the lower dial. This process can be repeated until all of the desired values of $10 + 5 \cdot L$ have been calculated. The process just described is known as the "continued method" of calculating. Obviously, a process of this sort reduces considerably the time required to perform a given series of calculations, and frequently much can be saved by employing the "continued method." For example, consider the equation

$$A_x = 1 - d \cdot a_x.$$

If the values of a_x are tabulated for several ages it is possible to apply the continued method to calculate the corresponding values of A_x at these ages. Here $J = 1$, $K = d$, and the values of L are the negatives of the annuity values. The number 1 is placed on the lower dial, the value of d is punched on the keyboard, and the crank is turned backward to form the successive values of $-a_x$ on the upper dial. The values of the result A_x are read at each stage from the lower dial.

EXERCISES—LIST XXXI

1. Check by the continued method the values of

$$A_x = 1 - d \cdot a_x$$

for ages 20 to 29, inclusive, as shown in Table IV, using the annuity values given in the same table.

2. Compute by the continued method the values of $A_{x:\overline{10}|}$ for ages 40 to 49, inclusive, using the formula

$$A_{x:\overline{10}|} = 1 - d \cdot a_{x:\overline{10}|}$$

with the temporary annuity values given in Table IX.

3. Check by the continued method the values of

$$v^n = 1 - i \cdot a_{\overline{n}|}$$

for values of n from 1 to 10, inclusive, as shown in Table I, using the annuity certain values given in the same table.

41. Tabulation of Reserves. The values of the terminal reserves for various policies are usually tabulated by life insurance companies in the form of a double-entry table. The following is an extract from such a table:

ORDINARY LIFE

Terminal Reserves per $1000 American Experience $3\frac{1}{2}\%$

Age at Issue	Net Premium	Reserve at End of Year						
		1	2	3	4	5	6	7
20	$13.47758	$6.19	$12.60	$19.24	$26.11	$33.23	$40.60	$48.24
21	13.77229	6.45	13.13	20.04	27.20	34.63	42.31	50.26
22	14.08122	6.72	13.68	20.89	28.36	36.09	44.09	52.38
23	14.40531	7.01	14.26	21.78	29.57	37.62	45.96	54.59
24	14.74558	7.31	14.88	22.72	30.83	39.23	47.92	56.91
25	15.10314	7.63	15.52	23.70	32.16	40.91	49.97	59.35
26	15.47921	7.96	16.19	24.72	33.54	42.67	52.11	61.89
etc.								

There are several methods in common use for the calculation of such a table for various types of policies, and some of these methods will now be considered in detail.

Ordinary Life.—*Diagonal method.* When the attained age $x + t$ is replaced by y, the prospective formula for the terminal reserve becomes

$$_tV_x = A_y - P_x \cdot a_y.$$

If the values of A_x, a_x, and P_x are available at various ages, this equation furnishes a convenient method of calculating reserves. One notes that for the reserves along a diagonal line in the table, the value of y is constant, and hence also the values of A_y and a_y are constant, while the value of P_x varies with the age at issue. Thus, the method of continued calculation described in the previous section can be applied directly.

Horizontal method. In § 36 the terminal reserve for the ordinary life policy was found to be (after replacing $x + t$ by y)

$$_tV_x = 1 - \frac{a_y}{a_x}.$$

When the annuity values are available, this equation may also be used to calculate, by a continued method, the reserves in a horizontal line in the table. When the value of x is held constant, the value of y varies with the policy year, and the terminal reserve is expressible in the form

$$J + K \cdot L,$$

with $J = 1$, $K = 1/a_x$, and $L = -a_y$.

Another convenient way of using the horizontal method for the continued computation of ordinary life reserves is to employ the identity

$$_{t+1}V_x = {}_tV_x - \frac{a_{x+t+1} - a_{x+t}}{a_x}.$$

The proof of the above identity is left to the student. If the difference $a_{x+t+1} - a_{x+t}$ is denoted by Δa_{x+t}, it follows that

$$_{t+1}V_x = {}_tV_x + (-\Delta a_{x+t})(1/a_x).$$

Numerical values of the quantity $-\Delta a_x$ are given in Table IV. The calculation begins with the punching of the value of $1/a_x$ upon the keyboard of the calculating machine. After turning the crank to register the positive number $-\Delta a_x$ in the upper dial, the lower dial gives the first terminal reserve, since with $t = 0$, the preceding equation becomes

$$_1V_x = (-\Delta a_x)(1/a_x).$$

The upper dial is now cleared, without disturbing the keyboard or lower dial, and the crank turned to register $-\Delta a_{x+1}$ in the upper dial. The lower dial now gives the second reserve, since with $t = 1$, we have

$$_2V_x = {}_1V_x + (-\Delta a_{x+1})(1/a_x).$$

In a similar manner the method is continued to give the numerical values of all of the desired reserves.

Endowment Policy.—In a manner similar to that used in § 36, the terminal reserve for an n year endowment policy may be expressed in the form,

$$(69) \qquad {}_tV_{x:\overline{n}|} = 1 - (a_{x+t:\overline{n-t}|})(1/a_{x:\overline{n}|}),$$

which, upon replacing $x + t$ by y, becomes

$${}_tV_{x:\overline{n}|} = 1 - (a_{y:\overline{n-t}|})(1/a_{x:\overline{n}|}).$$

If the temporary annuity values are available for all values of x and n, this formula affords a continued method of calculating terminal reserves appearing in a horizontal line of the table.

Endowment Policies Maturing at the Same Age.—From the prospective method the reserve for an endowment policy issued at age x and maturing at age z is found to be

$${}_tV_{x:\overline{z-x}|} = A_{y:\overline{z-y}|} - P_{x:\overline{z-x}|} \cdot a_{y:\overline{z-y}|},$$

where $y = x + t$. If the values of $A_{y:\overline{z-y}|}$, $P_{x:\overline{z-x}|}$, and $a_{y:\overline{z-y}|}$ are available, this formula may be used to calculate, by the continued method, all of the reserves appearing in a diagonal line of the table.

EXERCISES—LIST XXXII

1. Verify by the continued method all of the entries at age 20 shown in the table of reserves of § 41.

2. Verify by the continued method all of the entries, shown in the table of § 41, along a diagonal line beginning with the first terminal reserve at age 26.

3. Compute by the continued method the last five reserves for a $1000 ten year endowment policy issued at age 25.

4. For $1000 endowment policies maturing at age 60, compute:

(a) the net annual premiums at ages 20 to 25, inclusive, using the formula

$$P_{x:\overline{n}|} = \frac{1}{a_{x:\overline{n}|}} - d;$$

(b) all of the entries to be made in a table similar to that of § 41, the reserves to lie along a diagonal line beginning with the first terminal reserve at age 25.

42. Surrender Values. It has been mentioned that the terminal reserve plays an important role in determining the options allowed by an insurance company when the policyholder elects to discontinue his policy. There are usually three options available to the insured when such a surrender of the policy occurs:

(1) *Cash value*, an amount payable immediately upon surrender; or

(2) *Paid-up insurance*, a fully paid policy upon the original plan of insurance for a portion of the original amount; or

(3) *Extended insurance*, a fully paid policy for the original amount for a temporary period. (In event the cash value upon an endowment policy is sufficient to purchase extended insurance to the maturity date the excess, if any, is used to purchase pure endowment payable at the maturity date.)

The insurance laws of some of the states provide that these three options shall be actuarial equivalents, that is, they have the same value at the date of surrender. It is usual for the policy to provide that one of these three options, usually (3), shall be automatically in effect in event that the insured makes no choice.

It should be pointed out that insurance companies which sell insurance throughout the United States have forty-eight sets of laws to analyze and satisfy. These laws harmonize in a general way, but there are many particular requirements which vary from state to state. Policy provisions, which are acceptable in one state, are frequently illegal in other states.

The cash value is found by making a deduction, called the *surrender charge*, from the terminal reserve. Most state laws provide that the surrender charge after the second policy year cannot exceed $25 per $1000 of insurance. Some states restrict the surrender charge to 20% of the reserve. Companies differ in their methods of computing the surrender charge; however, it is customary to employ a decreasing scale of deductions and to make no surrender charge after a period which varies from five to twenty years.

Policies also provide for loans to the policyholder with the policy as security. The amount of the loan is, of course, limited by the cash value, and is deductible from the face amount of insurance in case of death or maturity of the policy.

Usually the cash value is obtained as the difference between the terminal reserve and the surrender charge; the paid-up insurance (option 2) is for an amount which the cash value of the policy will purchase upon the original plan; and the term of the extended insurance for the face amount of the policy (option 3) is determined so that the present value of the term insurance equals the cash value.

NUMERICAL EXAMPLES

1. The fifth terminal reserve for a $1000 ordinary life policy issued at age 25 is $40.91 on the basis of the A.E. $3\frac{1}{2}\%$ table. Assuming a surrender charge of $8.00, compute the three surrender options.

SOLUTION. At the end of the fifth policy year the age of the insured is 30.

(1)   Cash Value = Reserve − Surrender Charge
         = 40.91 − 8.00 = 32.91.

(2)   Amount of paid-up life insurance (employing Table IV)
         $= (32.91)(1/A_{30}) = (32.91)(2.967222) = 97.65.$

(3)   Term of extended insurance (interpolating in Table XI)

$1000A^1_{30:\overline{5}|} = 38.24$

$1000A^1_{30:\overline{4}|} = 31.06$

Diff. $= \overline{7.18}$

Difference per day $= \dfrac{7.18}{365} = 0.01967$

$32.91 − 31.06 = 1.85$

Number of days $= \dfrac{1.85}{0.01967} = 94.$

Hence the term of extended insurance is 4 years, 94 days.

2. The fifth terminal reserve for a $1000 ten year endowment policy issued at age 45 is $443.88 on the basis of the A.E. $3\frac{1}{2}\%$ table. Assuming a surrender charge of $10.88, compute the three surrender options.

SOLUTION. At the end of the fifth policy year the insured is age 50.

(1)   Cash Value $= 443.88 - 10.88 = 433.00$.

(2) Amount of paid-up endowment insurance maturing in five years. From Tables XI and VII, we find

$$1000A_{50:\overline{5}|} = 67.5987 + 778.7564 = 846.3551$$

Hence the amount of paid-up endowment insurance which the cash value $433.00 will purchase is

$$\frac{433.00}{0.8463551} = 511.61.$$

(3)   Extended insurance and pure endowment.

The cash value $433.00 is more than sufficient to purchase extended insurance for the five years elapsing before the policy matures. The excess (using Table XI),

$$433.00 - 1000A^1_{50:\overline{5}|} = 433.00 - 67.60$$
$$= 365.40,$$

is to be used to purchase pure endowment maturing at the end of five years.

$$\text{The amount of pure endowment} = (365.40)(1/_5E_{50})$$
$$= (365.40)(1.284099)$$
$$= 469.21.$$

Hence, option (3) provides for five years of extended insurance for the face amount of $1000 together with a pure endowment of $469.21 payable at the end of the five year period if the insured be then living.

EXERCISES—LIST XXXIII

1. Using the table of reserves shown in § 41 compute the three surrender options for each of the first six policy years on a $1000 ordinary life policy issued at age 20. Assume that the surrender charges are as follows: 1st and 2nd years, all of the reserve; 3rd year, $12.00; 4th year, $10.00; 5th year, $8.00; and 6th year, $6.00.

2. The fifth terminal reserve for a $1000 fifteen year endowment policy issued at age 40 is $265.03. Assuming a surrender charge of $7.03, compute the three surrender options.

3. The tenth terminal reserve for a $1000 fifteen year endowment policy issued at age 40 is $591.27. Assuming a surrender charge of $1.27, compute the three surrender options.

4. (a) Show that the amount of paid-up life insurance purchased by the tth terminal reserve for an ordinary life policy issued at age x is given by

$$1 - \frac{P_x}{P_{x+t}}.$$

(b) Show that the amount of paid-up endowment insurance purchased by the tth terminal reserve for an n year endowment policy issued at age x is given by

$$1 - \frac{P_{x:\overline{n}|}}{P_{x+t:\overline{n-t}|}}.$$

43. Mean Reserve. The term *mean reserve* is applied to the average of the initial and terminal reserves in any policy year. Thus the tth mean reserve is the average of the initial reserve for the tth policy year and the tth terminal reserve, and is equal to

$$\frac{t-1V + P + tV}{2}.$$

Life insurance companies are required, by the various state insurance departments, to file at the end of each calendar year a statement showing, in addition to other information, the total reserves on all outstanding policies. For convenience in the preparation of this statement, all policies issued in the same calendar year are assumed to have been issued at the middle of that calendar year (on July 1st). This assumption supposes that the policy year begins on July 1st of a calendar year and terminates on the succeeding July 1st. Since the date of valuation (December 31st) is midway between the beginning and end of the policy year, the reserve used is the average of the initial and terminal reserves, that is, the mean reserve. Thus, in a financial statement as of December 31, 1934, the first mean reserve would be used for all policies issued in 1934, the second mean reserve would be used for all policies issued in 1933, the third mean reserve for all policies issued in 1932, and so on. It should be observed that whenever the difference between the year of valuation and the year of issue is t, the $(t + 1)$th mean reserve is used.

EXERCISES—LIST XXXIV

1. Using the table given in § 41 compute the mean reserves for the first five policy years for a $1000 ordinary life policy issued at age 20.

REVIEW EXERCISES—LIST XXXV

1. Prove algebraically that the nth initial reserve for an n year endowment policy, face amount $1, is v, and give a verbal interpretation.

2. Find the terminal reserve of the fifth year on a twenty year endowment insurance for $1000 issued at age 20, with premiums payable for ten years.

3. A man now aged 45 has a $1000 twenty year endowment policy taken at age 30 and on which the terminal reserve is $664.91 at the end of the fifteenth policy year. If the company maintains reserves based upon the $3\frac{1}{2}\%$ A.E. table, what will be the terminal reserve at the end of the sixteenth policy year? The net annual premium is $39.51.

4. Assuming no surrender charge, show that the amount of paid-up insurance which may be given in event of the surrender, at the end of the tth policy year of an n payment life policy issued at age x, is given by the expression

$$1 - \frac{_nP_x}{_{n-t}P_{x+t}}.$$

5. Prove that

$$P_{x+t}(1 - {_tV_x}) = P_x + d \cdot {_tV_x},$$

and write down a similar relation which will hold for a twenty year endowment policy.

6. Given $P_{30} = 0.01828$; $P_{50} = 0.03636$; and $i = 3\%$, find the numerical value of $_{20}V_{30}$.

7. It is proposed that at the end of five years a twenty payment life policy issued at age x be changed to an endowment policy maturing at age $x + 20$ with future premiums equal to $P_{x:\overline{20}|}$ and that the payment to effect the change be an amount equal to the difference in net premiums accumulated at the valuation rate of interest. Assuming that only net premiums and reserves need to be taken into consideration, discuss this proposal and determine whether it is equitable or inequitable and to what extent.

8. Show that the tth terminal reserve for a policy issued at age x for a face amount of \$1, with an annual net premium of π, may be written in the form

$$A_{x+t} - \pi a_{x+t} + \frac{(\pi - P_x)N_x}{D_{x+t}},$$

if t years is less than or equal to the premium payment period.

9. A policy under which \$2000 will be paid on death before age 60, and \$1000 on death after age 60, is issued at age 30. The net annual premium is payable for twenty years. Find expressions in terms of commutation symbols for the 35th terminal reserve by both retrospective and prospective methods, and prove them equal.

10. By substituting commutation symbols for each term and simplifying, verify equation (64) for each of the following policies:

(a) ordinary life;

(b) twenty year endowment.

CHAPTER V

MODERN RESERVE SYSTEMS

44. Introduction. The premiums received by a life insurance company from the policyholder are, as mentioned in a previous chapter, gross premiums, made up of the net premium and an additional charge for expenses, called "loading." Since the gross premium is usually constant year after year and the net premium, under the level premium method, is also constant, the loading for expenses is necessarily the same in every policy year during the premium payment period. In the calculation of net premiums and reserves, the fact that the premiums collected are gross premiums, rather than net premiums, has been entirely ignored and the reserves already described in the previous sections are known as "net level premium reserves."

In dealing with policy reserves in this way, two tacit assumptions have been made, (a) that the whole of the net premium is available for the payment of death claims and for the maintenance of reserves, and (b) that no part of the loading is ever used for these purposes. Under practical conditions, as they exist in the United States, these assumptions are not correct. The major expenses incurred by a life insurance company in writing a policy must be met in the first policy year, while the expenses in the *renewal* years (the policy years following the first policy year) are comparatively small. In many cases the expense to be paid in the first year by the company exceeds the loading. Thus a company, in order to maintain net level reserves, would need to withdraw from its general surplus funds a sufficient amount to make up

103

the deficiency in loading for the first policy year. A small company might conceivably write a sufficiently large amount of new business so as to entirely deplete its surplus account and thereby become technically insolvent. Thus, a requirement of net level premium reserves for all life insurance companies would make it difficult, if not impossible, for new companies to survive the first few years following organization.

Several modifications of the net level premium reserve system have been adopted by various states as minimum legal standards for premiums and reserves. Some of these modifications will be considered in detail in this chapter.

Numerical Example. A certain life insurance company charges a gross premium of $16.25 for a $1000 ordinary life policy issued at age 25. In the first policy year the company pays the following expenses:

(a) Agent's commission: 50% of gross premium,
(b) State premium tax: 3% of gross premium,
(c) Medical examination: $2.50,
(d) Other expenses: $1.25.

Assuming that the company operates upon the net level premium reserve system based upon the American Experience 3½% table, find the amount that must be withdrawn from surplus for this policy in its first year?

SOLUTION.   The expenses total $12.36, made up of the items: commission, $8.12; tax, $.49; medical examination, $2.50; and other expenses $1.25. The net premium upon the basis stated is $15.10. During the first policy year the company must pay death claims and set up the net level reserve for each policy remaining in force at the end of the first year. Assuming the rate of mortality experienced by the company approximates that shown by the American Experience Table, it follows from equation (68) that the entire net level premium ($15.10) is needed to pay death claims and maintain the reserve. The total of the expenses and the net premium is $27.46, whereas the company collects only the gross premium of $16.25. Hence $11.21 must be withdrawn from surplus.

45. Modified Systems. A set of reserves, determined by any method which is not based upon a level net premium for all policy years during the premium payment period, is called a "modified reserve system." The procedure to be followed in this chapter in developing the subject of modified reserves is (a) the development of certain general relationships applicable to several of the more important types of modification, and (b), the specialization of these relationships to produce the individual systems.

It is convenient in the present discussion to consider an n payment m year endowment policy of amount one dollar issued at age x. By proper choice of the values of m and n, this policy may be specialized to any of the common plans of insurance issued by life insurance companies, except term policies.* Thus, when the m year endowment period is extended to the end of the mortality table, the policy becomes a limited payment life policy; when both m and n are extended to the end of the table, the policy becomes an ordinary life policy; when both m and n are chosen as twenty, the policy becomes a twenty year endowment policy, etc. The notation previously used to denote the net level premium for this policy is $_nP_{x:\overline{m}|}$, but for convenience the subscripts will be dropped, and the letter P will be used to indicate the net level premium for the policy under consideration.

Let us assume that a life insurance company sets aside, for the purpose of paying claims and maintaining reserves, a net premium of α in the first policy year, followed by a renewal net premium of β in each succeeding policy year for the re-

* As will be shown later, the application of the various modification principles to term policies is limited. Most life insurance companies use the net level reserve system on all term plans.

maining premium payment period. Under the net level reserve system the company would need to set aside a net premium of P in the first policy year, followed by a renewal net premium of the same amount in each succeeding year. Thus, the sequence of modified net premiums for the successive years,

$$\alpha, \beta, \beta, \beta, \cdots,$$

replaces the corresponding sequence of net level premiums

$$P, P, P, P, \cdots.$$

Since these two sets of net premiums provide for the same benefits, namely, m year endowment insurance, the present value of all the modified net premiums must be equal to the present value of all net level premiums, that is,

$$(70) \qquad P \cdot a_{x:\overline{n}|} = \alpha + \beta \cdot a_{x:\overline{n-1}|}.$$

Adding and subtracting β on the right side of this equation, we have

$$P \cdot a_{x:\overline{n}|} = \alpha - \beta + \beta(a_{x:\overline{n-1}|} + 1),$$

or

$$P \cdot a_{x:\overline{n}|} = \beta \cdot a_{x:\overline{n}|} - (\beta - \alpha).$$

Dividing this equation by $a_{x:\overline{n}|}$ and transposing, we get

$$(71) \qquad \beta - P = \frac{\beta - \alpha}{a_{x:\overline{n}|}}.$$

It is obvious from equation (71) that the difference between the two renewal net premiums, β and P, depends upon the value assigned to the difference between the modified renewal premium β and the first year modified premium α. In defining the various special types of modified reserve systems in the succeeding sections, specific values will be given to the difference $(\beta - \alpha)$. It is necessary to make the value of β larger than that assigned to α, so that the modification can relieve to some extent the additional burden of expense in the first policy year. From equation (71), it may be noted that when β is larger than α, the value of β is also larger than the net level premium P. Since the first year net premium must at least be sufficient to cover the cost of protection in that year, it is obvious that the value of α cannot be less than the one year term net premium, c_x.

46. Loading. It is worth-while to consider the modification of the net premiums and reserves from the viewpoint of the loading available to meet expenses in the various policy years. The diagram below is useful in understanding the effect of modification upon loading (P' indicates the gross premium):

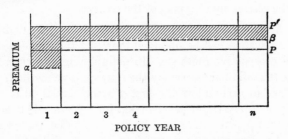

Under the modified system, the loading, represented by the shaded area, is $(P' - \alpha)$ for the first policy year and $(P' - \beta)$ for each renewal year, while under the net level system the loading is $(P' - P)$ for every year. Subtracting both members of equation (70) from $P'a_{x:\overline{n}|}$, we find

$$(P' - P) \cdot a_{x:\overline{n}|} = (P' - \alpha) + (P' - \beta)a_{x:\overline{n-1}|}.$$

A verbal interpretation of this equation shows that the present value of the loading under the two systems is precisely the same. Thus, in a sense, modification of net premiums means that a part of the loading available in the renewal years under the net level system is borrowed for additional expense in the first year, thereby reducing the loading available in the renewal years. In the modified system, the excess of first year loading over renewal year loading is

$$(P' - \alpha) - (P' - \beta) = \beta - \alpha.$$

It should be noted that a modification of premiums and reserves is employed solely for the purpose of providing for large preliminary expenses in the first policy year, and does not in any way affect the yearly amount of gross premium actually paid to the company by the policyholder. The modification is purely an internal transaction of the life insurance company, which releases a larger part of the gross premium for expenses in the first year and defers to a later date the setting up of a part of the reserve.

47. Modified Reserves. The terminal reserves under a modified system can be obtained by either the retrospective or the prospective methods. In determining an expression for the tth terminal reserve by the retrospective method, it is necessary to accumulate the first year net premium α with benefit of interest and survivorship for t years. This accumulation, upon referring to § 16, is $\alpha/{}_tE_x$. The sequence of renewal net premiums, viewed from the end of the tth year, form a foreborne annuity of annual rent β for $(t - 1)$ years, first payment at age $x + 1$, with an accumulated value of $\beta \cdot {}_{t-1}u_{x+1}$. The accumulated cost of the insurance, as in the net level system, is ${}_tk_x$. Thus, if ${}_tV'$ denotes the tth terminal reserve under the modified system, we obtain by the retrospective method, $(1 \leqq t \leqq n)$,

$$_tV' = \alpha \frac{1}{{}_tE_x} + \beta \cdot {}_{t-1}u_{x+1} - {}_tk_x,$$

which can be written in the form

$$(72) \qquad _tV' = \beta \cdot {}_tu_x - (\beta - \alpha) \frac{1}{{}_tE_x} - {}_tk_x,$$

since

$$_t u_x = _{t-1}u_{x+1} + \frac{1}{_t E_x}.$$

By the prospective method, we consider the difference in present values between the future benefits and future premiums, and we obtain

(73) $$_t V' = A_{x+t:\overline{m-t}|} - \beta \cdot a_{x+t:\overline{n-t}|}.$$

It is easily shown, by employing equation (71), that equations (72) and (73) produce equal values for the reserve.

It is possible to obtain a simple expression for the difference between the tth net level reserve and the corresponding modified reserve. Denote the net level reserve at the end of the tth policy year by $_t V$, and apply the prospective method to obtain

$$_t V = A_{x+t:\overline{m-t}|} - P \cdot a_{x+t:\overline{n-t}|}.$$

The corresponding modified reserve is

$$_t V' = A_{x+t:\overline{m-t}|} - \beta \cdot a_{x+t:\overline{n-t}|}.$$

Subtracting the second equation from the first, we obtain

$$_t V - _t V' = (\beta - P)a_{x+t:\overline{n-t}|},$$

or, referring to equation (71), we may write

(74) $$_t V - _t V' = (\beta - \alpha) \frac{a_{x+t:\overline{n-t}|}}{a_{x:\overline{n}|}}.$$

Since the difference $(\beta - \alpha)$ is positive in every modification, this equation shows that during the premium payment period the modified reserves are less than the corresponding net level reserves. Furthermore, the larger the difference $(\beta - \alpha)$, the larger will be the difference between the corresponding terminal reserves. As t increases, the difference between the net level terminal reserve and the corresponding modified reserve decreases, until finally at the end of the premium payment period the two reserves are equal.

EXERCISES—LIST XXXVI

1. (a) For a $1000 twenty payment life policy issued at age 30, compute the value of β, if α has a value of $10.00.

(b) For the policy in (a), what is the excess of the net *level* reserve over the modified reserve at the end of the tenth policy year?

SOLUTION. (a) Solving equation (71) for β, we obtain

$$\frac{1000_{20}P_{30} \cdot a_{30:\overline{20}|} - \alpha}{a_{30:\overline{20}|} - 1} = \frac{1000A_{30} - 10}{a_{30:\overline{20}|} - 1}$$

$$= \frac{337.0156 - 10}{12.63763} = \$25.8763.$$

(b) From equation (74) we obtain immediately

$$_{10}V - {_{10}}V' = (25.8763 - 10)\frac{a_{40:\overline{10}|}}{a_{30:\overline{20}|}} = \$9.59.$$

2. (a) For a $1000 twenty year endowment policy issued at age 30, compute the value of $(\beta - \alpha)$, if β is $1.25 more than the net level premium.

(b) For the policy in (a), what is the excess of the net level reserve over the modified reserve at the end of the tenth policy year?

3. For a $1000 fifteen year endowment policy issued at age 30, the difference between the renewal net premium and the first year net premium is $40.00. Compute the values of α and β and also the tenth modified reserve.

4. Prove that equations (72) and (73) give identical values for the reserves on an n payment m year endowment policy.

48. Full Preliminary Term. The so-called "Full Preliminary Term" (F.P.T.) system is a specialization of the general principles discussed in §§ 45–47. The subscript F will be used with the symbols α and β to indicate that full preliminary term net premiums are under consideration. Under the full preliminary term method of modifying premiums and reserves the first year net premium α_F for any given policy is assigned its minimum possible value, that is, α_F is chosen as the premium just sufficient to cover the cost of the death claims occurring during the first policy year. This value of α_F is the one year term premium, or natural premium c_x. Thus, the sequence of net level premiums

$$P, P, P, P, \cdots$$

is replaced under the full preliminary term method by the sequence of modified net premiums

$$c_x, \beta_F, \beta_F, \beta_F, \cdots.$$

Substituting

(75) $$c_x = \alpha$$

in equation (70), we obtain

$$P \cdot a_{x:\overline{n}|} = c_x + \beta_F \cdot a_{x:\overline{n-1}|}.$$

Since the value of the net level premium P is determined by the equation

$$P \cdot a_{x:\overline{m}|} = A_{x:\overline{m}|},$$

it follows that

$$c_x + \beta_F \cdot a_{x:\overline{n-1}|} = A_{x:\overline{m}|},$$

or, solving for β_F, we find

$$\beta_F = \frac{A_{x:\overline{m}|} - c_x}{a_{x:\overline{n-1}|}} = \frac{{}_1|A_{x:\overline{m-1}|}}{{}_1|a_{x:\overline{n-1}|}},$$

whence

(76) $$\beta_F = {}_{n-1}P_{x+1:\overline{m-1}|}.$$

A verbal interpretation of equation (76) shows that the renewal net premium under the full preliminary term system for a given policy is equal to the net level premium for a similar policy issued at an age one year higher, with premiums payable for a year less than the original premium payment period, and with the maturity of the policy at the same date as the original policy.

Upon substituting the value of β_F, given in equation (76), into equation (73), we see that

$$_tV' = A_{x+t:\overline{m-t}|} - {}_{n-1}P_{x+1:\overline{m-1}|} \cdot a_{x+t:\overline{n-t}|},$$

or

(77) $$_tV' = {}_{t-1:n-1}V_{x+1:\overline{m-1}|}, \qquad \text{for } 1 \leqq t \leqq n.$$

Thus, under the full preliminary term system the terminal reserve on a given policy at the end of the first year is zero, and, in general, the tth terminal full preliminary term reserve is the $(t-1)$th net level reserve for a policy issued at an age one year higher, with premiums payable for a year less than the original premium payment period and with the maturity of the policy at the same date as the original policy.

Equation (77) can also be derived by setting $\alpha = c_x$ in the equation preceding (72) in § 47. Doing so, we find

$$_tV' = c_x \frac{1}{_tE_x} + \beta \cdot {_{t-1}}u_{x+1} - {_t}k_x,$$

which can be written in the form

$$_tV' = \beta \cdot {_{t-1}}u_{x+1} - {_{t-1}}k_{x+1} = {_{t-1:n-1}}V_{x+1:\overline{m-1}|},$$

since

$$_tk_x = {_{t-1}}k_{x+1} + \frac{c_x}{_tE_x}; \qquad \beta = {_{n-1}}P_{x+1:\overline{m-1}|}.$$

It has been shown, by considering both net premiums and reserves, that the full preliminary term method implies that every policy is considered as a combination of two policies: (a) a one year term policy issued at the original age at issue x, for which the net premium is c_x and the first terminal reserve is zero, and (b), a level premium policy issued at an age one year higher, $x + 1$, providing for the balance of the benefits in the original policy, with premiums payable for the balance of the original premium payment period.

For the purpose of determining the net premiums and reserves, an ordinary life policy is considered under the full preliminary term system as a combination of a one year term policy followed by a net level ordinary life policy issued at the next age; a twenty year endowment policy is considered as a one year term policy followed by a net level nineteen year endowment policy at the next age; a twenty payment life policy is considered as a one year term policy followed by a net level nineteen payment life policy; and a twenty payment thirty year endowment policy is considered as a one year term policy followed by a net level nineteen payment twenty-nine year endowment.

It should be noted that after the expiration of the premium payment period the full preliminary term reserves are precisely those found by the net level premium system.

EXERCISES—LIST XXXVII

1. Compute by the prospective method the terminal reserve at the end of the fifth policy year for each of the following $1000 policies issued at age 35, using the full preliminary term system: (a) ordinary life; (b) twenty payment life.

2. Same as problem (1) using the retrospective method.

3. Compute the net level premium, the first year and renewal F.P.T. premiums, and the fifth net level and fifth F.P.T. terminal reserves for a $1000 ten year endowment policy issued at age 35.

4. Show that the tth terminal reserve for an ordinary life policy modified by the full preliminary term method may be expressed in the form

$$_tV' = 1 - \frac{a_{x+t}}{a_{x+1}}, \qquad \text{for} \quad t \geqq 1.$$

5. (a) Show that the tth terminal reserve for an n year endowment policy modified by the full preliminary term method may be expressed in the form

$$_tV' = 1 - \frac{a_{x+t:\overline{n-t}|}}{a_{x+1:\overline{n-1}|}}, \quad \text{for} \quad 1 \leqq t \leqq n.$$

(b) Use the equation of (a) to compute by the continued method all of the full preliminary term reserves for a $1000 five year endowment policy issued at age 25.

6. A certain ten payment endowment insurance policy issued at age 30 provides for $1000 in event of death during the first twenty policy years and $2000 in cash if the insured survives the twenty years. Using the full preliminary term modification, compute

(a) the values of α_F and β_F,

(b) the fifth terminal reserve by both prospective and retrospective methods.

49. Disadvantages of the Full Preliminary Term System.
In the full preliminary term system it is assumed that the whole of the first year's gross premium is used in paying expenses and death claims, and that no reserve need be set up at the end of that year. For an ordinary life policy issued at the younger ages the amount of loading released appears to be equitable, that is, it approximates the expense the life insurance company actually incurs in issuing the policy. Furthermore, the reduction in loading in the renewal years of the policy is not large and therefore does not materially reduce the expense allowance in the years following the first year.

However, further consideration of other plans of insurance and other ages at issue will show that the full preliminary term method of valuation is unsatisfactory in certain cases. For policies with relatively high premiums, such as short term endowment policies, the amount released for expense in the first year is far in excess of the amount actually required, and the application of the full preliminary term system to these policies might lead to extravagance on the part of the company. Furthermore, the increase in the net premium required for the renewal years of these policies is relatively large, and materially reduces the loading available for expense in these years.

These considerations have led, in many states, to the adoption of statutes permitting the use of the full preliminary term system for policies having relatively low premiums, while for higher premium plans other modifications are required.

50. Ordinary Life Modification. Another specialization of the general principles discussed in §§ 45–47 is the "ordinary life modification," sometimes referred to as the "modified preliminary term" system. The subscript O will be used with the symbols α and β to indicate that the ordinary life modication is under consideration. Under this system the sequence of modified net premiums

$$\alpha_O, \beta_O, \beta_O, \beta_O, \cdots,$$

which replaces the sequence of net level premiums

$$P, P, P, P, \cdots,$$

is selected, regardless of the plan of insurance under consideration, so that

$$(78) \qquad \beta_O - \alpha_O = P_{x+1} - c_x,$$

where P_{x+1} is invariably the net annual premium for an ordinary life policy at age $x + 1$ and c_x is the natural premium at age x. Numerical values of the differences $(P_{x+1} - c_x)$ are given in Table V.

It will be observed from equation (78) that the difference $(\beta_O - \alpha_O)$ for any given policy is equal to the difference between the renewal net premium and the first year net premium for a corresponding ordinary life policy modified on the full preliminary term system. It is common practice not to apply this modification to term policies, but to use the full preliminary term system or the net level system for these plans.

Replacing the difference $\beta_O - \alpha_O$ by $P_{x+1} - c_x$ in equation (71), we obtain

$$\beta_O - P = \frac{P_{x+1} - c_x}{a_{x:\overline{n}|}},$$

and hence

$$(79) \qquad \beta_O = P + \frac{P_{x+1} - c_x}{a_{x:\overline{n}|}},$$

from which the value of β_O can be computed. After computing β_O from equation (79), the first year net premium α_O is found from equation (78).

The numerical values of α_O and β_O for a given policy can now be inserted in either of the expressions for the terminal reserve obtained in § 47. Thus, when the retrospective method is used, the tth terminal reserve is computed from

$$(72') \qquad {}_tV' = \beta_O \cdot {}_tu_x - (\beta_O - \alpha_O)\frac{1}{{}_tE_x} - {}_tk_x.$$

However, the prospective formula,

$$(73') \qquad {}_tV' = A_{x+t:\overline{m-t}|} - \beta_O \cdot a_{x+t:\overline{n-t}|},$$

is somewhat shorter in numerical computation, since it involves one term less than the retrospective formula (72').

When the terminal reserves on the modified preliminary term basis are to be computed sequentially, Fackler's Accumulation Formula may be applied directly. Thus, referring to § 37, the first terminal reserve is computed by means of the equation

$$_1V' = \alpha_O \cdot u_x - k_x,$$

and the successive terminal reserves, following the first, are obtained from the formula

$$_{t+1}V' = ({}_tV' + \beta_O)u_{x+t} - k_{x+t},$$

for the successive values $t = 1, 2, \cdots, (n-1)$.

EXERCISES—LIST XXXVIII

1. For a \$1000 twenty year endowment policy issued at age 40 and modified on the ordinary life basis, compute:

(a) the first year and renewal net premiums;

(b) the tenth terminal reserve by the prospective method;

(c) the tenth terminal reserve by the retrospective method.

SOLUTION. (a) The net level annual premium for this policy is computed by means of the formula

$$1000P_{40:\overline{20}|} = 1000\left(\frac{1}{a_{40:\overline{20}|}} - d\right)$$

from which, by Table IX, we find

$$1000P_{40:\overline{20}|} = \frac{1000}{13.33479} - 33.81643 = 41.17538.$$

Substituting the value of

$$\beta - \alpha = 1000(P_{41} - c_{40}) = 14.89336,$$

obtained from Table V into equation (79), we get

$$\beta = 41.17538 + \frac{14.89336}{13.33479} = 42.29226.$$

The first year net premium, found by means of equation (78), is

$$\alpha = 42.29226 - 14.89336 = 27.39890.$$

(b) Applying the formula (73) to find the tenth modified reserve, we have, by Tables XI, VII, and IX,

$$_{10}V' = 1000A_{50:\overline{10}|} - \beta \cdot a_{50:\overline{10}|}$$
$$= 139.7360 + 588.1962 - (42.29226)(8.045433)$$
$$= \$387.67.$$

(c) Similarly, the retrospective formula (72) yields, by Tables X, VIII, and XII,

$$_{10}V' = \beta \cdot {}_{10}u_{40} - (\beta - \alpha)\frac{1}{_{10}E_{40}} - 1000 \cdot {}_{10}k_{40}$$

$$= (42.29226)(13.00173) - (14.89336)(1.578366) - 138.6934$$
$$= \$387.67.$$

2. For a \$1000 ten year endowment policy issued at age 40 and modified on the ordinary life basis, compute:

(a) the first year and renewal net premiums;

(b) the fifth terminal reserve by the retrospective method;

(c) the fifth terminal reserve by the prospective method.

3. Find the tenth and twenty-fifth terminal reserves modified on the ordinary life basis for a \$1000 fifteen payment thirty year endowment policy issued at age 25.

4. For an n payment m year endowment policy issued at age x and modified on the ordinary life basis, show that

$$\beta_O = \frac{A_{x:\overline{m}|} + (P_{x+1} - c_x)}{a_{x:\overline{n}|}}.$$

5. Use Fackler's Accumulation Formula to compute all of the reserves modified on the ordinary life basis for a \$1000 ten year endowment policy issued at age 30.

6. If $a'_{x:\overline{n}|}$ denotes the fraction

$$\frac{a_{x:\overline{n}|}}{1 + P_{x+1} - c_x},$$

show that for an n year endowment policy modified on the ordinary life basis

(a) $\beta_O = \dfrac{1}{a'_{x:\overline{n}|}} - d,$ \qquad\qquad (b) $_tV' = 1 - \dfrac{a_{x+t:\overline{n-t}|}}{a'_{x:\overline{n}|}}.$

7. Using the equations of problem (6) compute by a continued method the 5th to 10th modified reserves, inclusive, for a \$1000 ten year endowment policy issued at age 25.

51. Other Properties of the Ordinary Life Modification. Some interesting properties of the ordinary life modification can be obtained from the relations presented in the previous section. The equation

$$(79) \qquad\qquad \beta_O = P + \frac{P_{x+1} - c_x}{a_{x:\overline{n}|}},$$

which determines the value of β_O, implies that the net renewal premium β_O under this modification exceeds the net level premium for the same policy by an amount which depends upon the number of annual premiums and the age at issue, but this amount is entirely independent of the type or duration of the benefits provided by the policy. For example, $\beta_O - P$ is the same for all twenty payment policies issued at a given age x, whether the benefit provided is whole life insurance or endowment insurance.

Substituting the value of $\beta_O - \alpha_O$ from equation (78) into equation (74), we find

$$(80) \qquad\qquad _tV - {_tV'} = (P_{x+1} - c_x) \frac{a_{x+t:\overline{n-t}|}}{a_{x:\overline{n}|}}.$$

A verbal interpretation of this equation shows that the excess of the net level reserve over the corresponding modified reserve depends for its value upon the age at issue x, the number of premiums n, and the duration t at which the reserve is to be taken, but does not depend upon the type or duration of the benefits provided by the policy. This difference, for example, is the same for the tenth terminal reserves on a twenty year endowment, a twenty payment life policy, and a twenty payment thirty year endowment policy, assuming all of the policies to be issued at the same age. It should be observed that the right member of equation (80) can be computed by means of the continued method of calculation described in section (40).

A supplementary point of view with respect to the modified preliminary term system may be obtained by considering the first year net premium α_O as the sum of the natural premium c_x and a second quantity to be denoted by π. Thus

$$(81) \qquad \alpha_O = c_x + \pi,$$

and since

$$\beta_O = \alpha_O + (P_{x+1} - c_x),$$

it follows that

$$(82) \qquad \beta_O = P_{x+1} + \pi.$$

Substituting these values for α_O and β_O in equation (72), we find

$$(83) \qquad {}_tV' = (P_{x+1} + \pi)\,{}_tu_x - (P_{x+1} - c_x)\,\frac{1}{{}_tE_x} - {}_tk_x.$$

Employing the two identities

$$ {}_tu_x = {}_{t-1}u_{x+1} + \frac{1}{{}_tE_x} $$

$$ {}_tk_x = {}_{t-1}k_{x+1} + c_x \cdot \frac{1}{{}_tE_x}, $$

we may write equation (83) in the form

$$ {}_tV' = (P_{x+1} \cdot {}_{t-1}u_{x+1} - {}_{t-1}k_{x+1}) + \pi \cdot {}_tu_x, $$

or

$$(84) \qquad {}_tV' = {}_{t-1}V_{x+1} + \pi \cdot {}_tu_x.$$

Equation (84) implies that the tth terminal reserve on the modified basis may be considered as the tth full preliminary term reserve on an ordinary life policy issued at the same age increased by the accumulation, with interest and benefit of survivorship, of a level extra premium π. Thus, the first year modified reserve is $\pi \cdot u_x$; the second modified reserve is $\pi \cdot {}_2u_x + {}_1V_{x+1}$; the third modified reserve is $\pi \cdot {}_3u_x + {}_2V_{x+1}$; and so on. At the end of the premium payment period the modified reserve and the net level reserve are equal, and hence it follows that

$$\pi \cdot {}_nu_x + {}_{n-1}V_{x+1} = A_{x+n:\overline{m-n}|}.$$

Solving this equation for π, we have

$$(85) \qquad \pi = \frac{A_{x+n:\overline{m-n}|} - {}_{n-1}V_{x+1}}{{}_nu_x},$$

an equation from which the value of π may be determined. The values of α_O and β_O can now be computed from equations (81) and (82), and the modified terminal reserves follow from equation (84). This method of computing the modified reserves is particularly useful when the values of the ordinary life reserves are available.

EXERCISES—LIST XXXIX

1. For a \$1000 twenty payment life policy issued at age 45 and modified on the ordinary life basis, compute
   (a) the numerical values of π, α_O, and β_O,
   (b) the fifteenth terminal reserve by means of equation (84).

SOLUTION. (a) For this particular policy, equation (85) gives, by use of Tables IV and X,

$$\pi = \frac{1000(A_{65} - {}_{19}V_{46})}{{}_{20}u_{45}} = \frac{1000A_{65} - 1000\left(1 - \dfrac{a_{65}}{a_{46}}\right)}{{}_{20}u_{45}}$$

$$= \frac{688.2364 - 1000\left(1 - \dfrac{9.219295}{15.791058}\right)}{38.89932} = 6.99412.$$

From equations (81) and (82), we can compute, by Tables VI and V, respectively,

$$\alpha_O = 10.78560 + 6.99412 = 17.77972,$$

and

$$\beta_O = 29.51055 + 6.99412 = 36.50467.$$

(b) Applying equation (84) to this particular policy, we obtain, by Table X,

$$_{15}V' = 1000\,_{14}V_{46} + \pi \cdot \,_{15}u_{45}$$

$$= 1000\left(1 - \frac{a_{60}}{a_{46}}\right) + (6.99412)(23.48303)$$

$$= 301.3515 + 164.2431 = 465.5946.$$

For a check upon the reserve value, we use Table IV and the prospective formula

$$_{15}V' = 1000A_{60} - \beta_O \cdot a_{60:\overline{5}|}$$

$$= 626.9237 - (36.50467)(4.419409) = 465.5946.$$

2. For a $1000 twenty-five year endowment policy issued at age 25 and modified on the ordinary life basis,

(a) compute the numerical values of β_O and α_O by means of equations (78) and (79);

(b) compute the fifteenth terminal reserve by means of equation (72′);

(c) compute the fifteenth terminal reserve by means of equation (73′);

(d) compute the value of π from equation (85);

(e) check the value of π by verifying equations (81) and (82);

(f) compute the fifteenth terminal reserve by means of equation (84);

(g) compute the fifteenth terminal reserve by means of equation (80).

3. A $1000 ten payment thirty year endowment policy issued at age 30 is to be modified on the ordinary life basis. Then

(a) compute the value of π;

(b) find the fifth terminal reserve by means of equation (84);

(c) check the value found in (b) by the prospective method;

(d) check the value found in (b) by the retrospective method.

4. Fill in the missing values in the following table assuming all policies to be issued at the same age for the same amount and under the same assumptions regarding mortality and interest:

Policy	Net Level Premium	5th Net Level Reserve	α_O	β_O	5th Res. O.L. Mod.
10 payt. life	$44.77	$204.80	$34.31	$46.21	$198.21
10 yr. endowment	87.02	446.15			
10 payt. 15 yr. end.	75.02	377.59			
10 payt. 20 yr. end.	65.56	323.58			
10 payt. end. at 60	58.28	281.95			
10 payt. end. at 65	52.87	251.04			

5. (a) Show that for any n payment policy modified on the ordinary life basis

$$\pi = (\beta_F - P_{x+1}) \frac{a_{x:\overline{n-1}|}}{a_{x:\overline{n}|}}.$$

(b) In view of the equation found in (a) show that $\alpha_O > c_x$, if and only if $\beta_F > P_{x+1}$.

(c) Explain why a modification on the ordinary life basis is impractical for a term policy which has a full preliminary term net renewal premium which is less than P_{x+1}.

6. Compute the values of π for each of the following $1000 policies issued at age 30:

(a) thirty payment life;

(b) thirty year endowment;

(c) ten payment endowment maturing at age 65.

7. For a $1000 twenty year endowment policy issued at age 45 find the fifteenth terminal reserve on the net level basis. By employing equation (80) find the value of the fifteenth reserve modified on the ordinary life basis.

52. Twenty Payment Life Modification.

Another specialization of the general principles discussed in §§ 45–47 is the "twenty payment life modification." The methods which have been considered in the previous sections provide for a modification of premiums and reserves extending over the entire premium payment period. In contrast with this procedure, the twenty payment life modification provides for a modification of premiums and reserves over a period of years, not to exceed twenty. The subscript I will be used with the symbols α and β to indicate that the twenty payment life modification is under consideration. Under this system the sequence of modified net premiums

$$(86) \qquad \alpha_I, \beta_I, \beta_I, \cdots, \beta_I, P, P, \cdots$$

(the largest possible number of net premiums of β_I in sequence (86) being 19), which replaces the corresponding sequence of net level premiums

$$P, P, P, \cdots, P, P, P, \cdots,$$

is selected so that

$$(87) \qquad \beta_I - \alpha_I = {}_{19}P_{x+1} - c_x,$$

regardless of the plan of insurance under consideration. It will be observed from equation (87) that the difference $(\beta_I - \alpha_I)$ for any given policy is equal to the difference between the renewal net premium and the first year net premium for a corresponding full preliminary term twenty payment life policy. For certain policies, having relatively low premiums, the application of the twenty payment life modification would produce a value for α_I which is less than the natural premium c_x. For such a policy it is apparent that the twenty payment life modification is not practical, and it is customary, in these cases, to use the full preliminary term system or the net level system.

All policies to be modified by the twenty payment life method fall naturally into two cases: (a) those with twenty premiums or less, and (b) those with twenty or more premiums. The two cases will be considered individually in the following sections.

53. Policies with Twenty Premiums or Less. If the number of premiums, n, for a given policy is less than or equal to twenty, equation (71), when the difference $(\beta_I - \alpha_I)$ is replaced by $({}_{19}P_{x+1} - c_x)$, yields

$$\beta_I - P = \frac{{}_{19}P_{x+1} - c_x}{a_{x:\overline{n}}},$$

or

$$(88) \qquad \beta_I = P + \frac{_{19}P_{x+1} - c_x}{a_{x:\overline{n}|}},$$

an equation from which the value of β_I is determined. After computing β_I from equation (88), the first year net premium α_I is found from equation (87). Numerical values of the differences $(_{19}P_{x+1} - c_x)$ are given in Table V.

The numerical values of α_I and β_I for a given policy can now be inserted in either of the expressions for the terminal reserve obtained in § 47. Thus, the tth terminal reserve can be computed from the retrospective formula $(1 \leqq t \leqq n)$

$$(72'') \qquad _tV' = \beta_I \cdot {_tu_x} - (\beta_I - \alpha_I)\frac{1}{_tE_x} - {_tk_x},$$

or from the prospective formula

$$(73'') \qquad _tV' = A_{x+t:\overline{m-t}|} - \beta_I \cdot a_{x+t:\overline{n-t}|}.$$

When the reserves on the twenty payment life modification are to be computed sequentially, Fackler's Accumulation Formula may be applied directly, as in the ordinary life modification.

EXERCISES—LIST XL

1. For a $1000 fifteen year endowment policy issued at age 35 and modified on the twenty payment life basis, compute:

    (a) the first year and renewal net premiums;

    (b) the tenth terminal reserve by the prospective method;

    (c) the tenth terminal reserve by the retrospective method.

SOLUTION. (a) The net level premium is calculated by means of the identity

$$1000P_{35:\overline{15}|} = 1000\left(\frac{1}{a_{35:\overline{15}|}} - d\right)$$

$$= \frac{1000}{11.21251} - 33.81643 = 55.36967. \qquad \text{(Table IX.)}$$

Substituting the value of

$$\beta_I - \alpha_I = 1000(_{19}P_{36} - c_{35}) = 20.24806.$$

obtained from Table V into equation (88), we obtain

$$\beta_I = 55.36967 + \frac{20.24806}{11.21251} = 57.1755.$$

The value of α_I, obtained from equation (87), is

$$\alpha_I = 57.1755 - 20.2481 = 36.9274.$$

(b) Applying the prospective formula (73''), we have, by Tables XI, VII, and IX,

$$_{10}V' = 1000A_{45:\overline{5}|} - \beta_I \cdot a_{45:\overline{5}|}$$
$$= 53.08709 + 792.3786 - (57.1755)(4.569802) = 584.185.$$

(c) Similarly, the retrospective formula (72'') yields, by Tables X, VIII, and XII,

$$_{10}V' = \beta_I \cdot {_{10}}u_{35} - (\beta_I - \alpha_I)\frac{1}{_{10}E_{35}} - 1000{_{10}}k_{35}$$
$$= (57.1755)(12.87760) - (20.24806)(1.556065) - 120.5907$$
$$= 584.185.$$

2. Show that the net renewal premium for an n payment m year endowment policy ($n \leq 20$), modified on the twenty payment life basis, may be expressed in the form

$$\beta_I = \frac{A_{x:\overline{m}|} + ({_{19}}P_{x+1} - c_x)}{a_{x:\overline{n}|}}.$$

3. Compute the first year and renewal net premiums for the twenty payment life modification of each of the following $1000 policies issued at age 30: (a) ten payment twenty year endowment; (b) ten payment life; (c) fifteen payment life.

4. If $a'_{x:\overline{n}|}$ denotes the fraction

$$\frac{a_{x:\overline{n}|}}{1 + {_{19}}P_{x+1} - c_x},$$

show that for an n year endowment policy modified on the twenty payment life basis ($n \leq 20$)

(a) $\beta_I = \dfrac{1}{a'_{x:\overline{n}|}} - d;$ \qquad\qquad (b) $_tV' = 1 - \dfrac{a_{x+t:\overline{n-t}|}}{a'_{x:\overline{n}|}}.$

5. Using the equations of Exercise 4, compute the modified reserves for the fifth to tenth years, inclusive, by a continued method for a $1000 ten year endowment policy issued at age 25.

6. Use Fackler's Accumulation Formula to compute all of the reserves modified on the twenty payment life basis for a $1000 ten year endowment policy issued at age 25.

7. Find the tenth and twenty-fifth terminal reserves modified on the twenty payment life basis for a $1000 fifteen payment thirty year endowment policy issued at age 35.

54. Policies with Twenty or More Premiums. As stated in section (52) the twenty payment life modification requires that the net premiums payable after the twentieth policy year be net level premiums. Upon comparing the sequence of modified net premiums (86), with the corresponding sequence of net level premiums for the same policy, it is apparent that the present value of the first twenty premiums in the two sequences must be equal. Hence, we may write

$$P \cdot a_{x:\overline{20}|} = \alpha_I + \beta_I \cdot a_{x:\overline{19}|},$$

for any policy providing for twenty or more premiums. Adding and subtracting β_I on the right side of this equation and dividing by $a_{x:\overline{20}|}$, we find

$$(89) \qquad \beta_I = P + \frac{\beta_I - \alpha_I}{a_{x:\overline{20}|}}.$$

From the definition of the modification as stated in equation (87) it is evident equation (89) can be written in the form

$$(90) \qquad \beta_I = P + \frac{{}_{19}P_{x+1} - c_x}{a_{x:\overline{20}|}},$$

from which the value of β_I can be computed. Transposing the terms of equation (87) we use for the computation of the first year net premium

$$\alpha_I = \beta_I - ({}_{19}P_{x+1} - c_x).$$

As in the preceding modifications the tth terminal reserve can be computed from the retrospective formula $(1 \leqq t \leqq 20)$

$$(72'') \qquad {}_tV' = \beta_I \cdot {}_t u_x - (\beta_I - \alpha_I) \frac{1}{{}_t E_x} - {}_t k_x.$$

In writing an expression for the tth terminal reserve, for $t \leqq 20$, by the prospective method, it is necessary to recognize the change in net premiums which occurs at the end of the twentieth year. The future net premiums constitute a temporary annuity of β_I per year for $(20 - t)$ years and a deferred temporary annuity of P per year for the balance of the premium payment period. Thus, one obtains for the tth modified reserve by the prospective method

$$(91) \quad _tV' = A_{x+t:\overline{m-t}|} - \beta_I \cdot a_{x+t:\overline{20-t}|} - P \cdot {}_{20-t}|a_{x+t:\overline{n-20}|}.$$

The tth modified reserve, for values of t greater than or equal to twenty, is the corresponding net level reserve, since the future net premiums are identical under the two systems.

It should be noted that equation (90) is a special case of equation (88) with $n = 20$.

EXERCISES—LIST XLI

1. For a \$1000 twenty-five year endowment policy issued at age 20 and modified on the twenty payment life basis, compute:

(a) the three net premiums α_I, β_I, and P;

(b) the tenth terminal reserve by the retrospective method;

(c) the twenty-third terminal reserve by the prospective method.

2. A twenty payment policy issued at age 40 provides for \$1000 insurance for thirty years and a \$800 pure endowment at the end of this period. Using the twenty payment life modification, find:

(a) the first year and renewal net premiums;

(b) the tenth terminal reserve by both the retrospective and prospective methods.

55. Twenty Payment Life Modification—Other Properties. Some interesting properties of the twenty payment life modification can be obtained from the relations presented in the previous sections. The two equations

$$(88) \qquad \beta_I = P + \frac{{}_{19}P_{x+1} - c_x}{a_{x:\overline{n}|}}, \qquad \text{for } n \leqq 20,$$

and

$$(90) \qquad \beta_I = P + \frac{{}_{19}P_{x+1} - c_x}{a_{x:\overline{20}|}}, \qquad \text{for } n \geqq 20,$$

imply that the net renewal premium β_I under this modification exceeds the net level premium P for the same policy by an amount which depends upon the age at issue x and, if $n < 20$, upon the number of annual premiums n, but this excess is entirely independent of the type or duration of the benefits provided by the policy. Thus, for example, the value of $(\beta_I - P)$ is constant for all ten payment policies issued at a given age x, whether the benefit provided is whole life insurance or endowment insurance. Furthermore, the difference $(\beta_I - P)$ is constant for all policies issued at the same age x having premiums payable to twenty years or more.

Subtracting each of the equations $(73'')$ and (91) from the prospective formula for the net level reserve

$$_tV = A_{x+t:\overline{m-t}|} - P \cdot a_{x+t:\overline{n-t}|},$$

we obtain expressions for the difference between the tth terminal reserves under the net level system and the modified system, namely, $(t < 20)$

$$(92) \qquad _tV - {}_tV' = \left(\frac{_{19}P_{x+1} - c_x}{a_{x:\overline{n}|}} \right) a_{x+t:\overline{n-t}|}, \qquad \text{for } n \leqq 20,$$

and

$$(93) \qquad _tV - {}_tV' = \left(\frac{_{19}P_{x+1} - c_x}{a_{x:\overline{20}|}} \right) a_{x+t:\overline{20-t}|}, \qquad \text{for } n \geqq 20.$$

A verbal interpretation of these equations implies that the excess of the net level reserve over the corresponding modified reserve depends for its value upon the age at issue x, the duration t at which the reserves are to be taken, and, if $n < 20$, upon the number of annual premiums. The difference, for example, between the fifth net level reserve and the fifth modified reserve is the same for a ten payment life policy, a ten year endowment policy, and a ten payment twenty year endowment policy, assuming all the policies to be issued at the same age. Furthermore, the difference between the fifth net level reserve and the fifth modified reserve is the same for a twenty payment life policy, a twenty year endowment policy, a twenty-five year endowment policy, etc., assuming all the policies to be issued at the same age.

It should be observed that after the value of the fraction

$$\frac{{}_{19}P_{x+1} - c_x}{a_{x:\overline{n}|}}$$

has been computed for a given age at issue and a given value of n, the right members of equations (92) and (93) may be computed for successive values of t by the continued method described in § 40.

56. Twenty Payment Life Modification—Extra Premium. A supplementary point of view with respect to the twenty payment life modification may be obtained by considering the first year net premium α_I as the sum of the natural premium c_x and a second quantity to be denoted by π'. Thus one writes

$$(94) \qquad \alpha_I = c_x + \pi',$$

and since

$$\beta_I = \alpha_I + ({}_{19}P_{x+1} - c_x),$$

it follows that

$$(95) \qquad \beta_I = {}_{19}P_{x+1} + \pi',$$

regardless of the value of n. Substituting these values of α_I and β_I in equation (72'') we find, for $t \leqq 20$,

$$(96) \quad {}_tV' = ({}_{19}P_{x+1} + \pi')\, {}_tu_x - ({}_{19}P_{x+1} - c_x)\, \frac{1}{{}_tE_x} - {}_tk_x.$$

Employing the two identities

$$ {}_tu_x = {}_{t-1}u_{x+1} + \frac{1}{{}_tE_x}, \qquad {}_tk_x = {}_{t-1}k_{x+1} + \frac{c_x}{{}_tE_x},$$

we may write equation (96) in the form

$$ {}_tV' = ({}_{19}P_{x+1} \cdot {}_{t-1}u_{x+1} - {}_{t-1}k_{x+1}) + \pi' \cdot {}_tu_x,$$

or

$$(97) \qquad {}_tV' = {}_{t-1:19}V_{x+1} + \pi' \cdot {}_tu_x.$$

Equation (97) implies that the tth terminal reserve ($t \leqq 20$) under the twenty payment life modification may be considered as the tth full preliminary term reserve on a twenty payment life policy issued at the same age increased by the accumulation, with interest and benefit of survivorship, of a level extra premium π'. Thus, the first year modified reserve is $\pi' \cdot u_x$; the second modified reserve is $\pi' \cdot {}_2u_x + {}_{1:19}V_{x+1}$; the third modified reserve is $\pi' \cdot {}_3u_x + {}_{2:19}V_{x+1}$; and so on.

If the number of premiums n is less than twenty, the modified reserve at the end of the premium payment period is equal to the net level reserve; hence it follows that

$$\pi' \cdot {}_nu_x + {}_{n-1:19}V_{x+1} = A_{x+n:\overline{m-n}|}.$$

If this equation is solved for the value of π', there results

$$(98) \qquad \pi' = \frac{A_{x+n:\overline{m-n}|} - {}_{n-1:19}V_{x+1}}{{}_nu_x}, \qquad (n \leqq 20).$$

from which the value of π' can be determined. If, however, the number of premiums n is equal to or greater than twenty, the modified reserve at the end of the twentieth year is equal to the net level reserve, and hence

$$\pi' \cdot {}_{20}u_x + {}_{19:19}V_{x+1} = {}_{20}V.$$

Solving this equation for the value of π', we obtain

$$\pi' = \frac{{}_{20}V - {}_{19:19}V_{x+1}}{{}_{20}u_x},$$

or

$$(99) \qquad \pi' = \frac{{}_{20}V - {}_{20:20}V_x}{{}_{20}u_x} = \frac{{}_{20}V - A_{x+20}}{{}_{20}u_x}, \qquad (n \geqq 20).$$

Replacing the two reserves appearing in the right member of this equation by the corresponding retrospective formulas, we may write equation (99) in the form

$$\pi' = \frac{(P \cdot {_{20}}u_x - {_{20}}k_x) - ({_{20}}P_x \cdot {_{20}}u_x - {_{20}}k_x)}{{_{20}}u_x},$$

or, upon simplification,

(100) $\pi' = P - {_{20}}P_x,$ $(n \geqq 20).$

Equations (98) and (100) give, for $n < 20$ and $n \geqq 20$ respectively, methods of computing the value of π'. After the value of π' has been determined for a given policy by means of (98) or (100), the values of α_I and β_I can then be computed from equations (94) and (95). The terminal reserves upon the twenty payment life modification are obtained by means of equations (97). This method of computing the modified reserves is particularly useful when the values of the full preliminary term twenty payment life reserves are available.

EXERCISES—LIST XLII

1. For a twenty payment m year endowment policy modified on the twenty payment life basis, show that

$$\pi' = \frac{D_{x+m} - M_{x+m}}{N_x - N_{x+20}}.$$

2. For a policy having less than twenty premiums and modified on the twenty payment life basis, show that

$$\pi' = (\beta_F - {_{19}}P_{x+1})\frac{a_{x:\overline{n-1}|}}{a_{x:\overline{m}|}}.$$

3. For a \$1000 twenty-five year endowment policy issued at age 30 and modified on the twenty payment life basis, compute:

(a) the numerical values of β_I and α_I by means of equations (90) and (87), respectively;

(b) the fifteenth terminal reserve by means of equation (72'');

(c) the value of π' from equation (100);

(d) check the value of π' by verifying equation (94);

(e) compute the fifteenth terminal reserve by means of equation (97);

(f) find the value of the fifteenth terminal reserve by means of equation (93).

4. Compute the value of π' for each of the following $1000 policies issued at age 25: (a) twenty-five year endowment; (b) thirty year endowment.

5. For a twenty year endowment show that

(a) $\beta_I = P_{x:\overline{20}|} + ({}_{19}P_{x+1} - {}_{20}P_x)$;

(b) ${}_tV' = {}_tV_{x:\overline{20}|} + ({}_{t-1:19}V_{x+1} - {}_{t:20}V_x)$.

57. Illinois Standard. Several states have adopted as a minimum standard for reserves the so-called "Illinois Standard" system of modification. Under this system policies are divided into two groups:

(a) policies with premiums less than or equal to the premium for a twenty payment life policy issued at the same age,

(b) policies with premiums greater than or equal to the premium for a twenty payment life policy issued at the same age.

The minimum reserve permitted by the Illinois Standard for policies falling in group (a) is the full preliminary term reserve, whereas policies in group (b) must have reserves at least as high as those obtained by the twenty payment life modification. It should be observed that the twenty payment life policy is included in both groups (a) and (b), since for this policy the full preliminary term system and the twenty payment life modification give identical reserves.

It is apparent, after a little consideration, that life and endowment policies falling into group (a) are (with the exception of the twenty payment life policy) policies with premium payment periods of more than twenty years. An attempt to apply the twenty payment life modification to such a policy would, according to equation (100), lead to a negative value for π', and hence produce a first year net premium α_I which is insufficient to cover the tabular cost of the insurance for the first year.

58. New Jersey Standard. Several plans of insurance commonly issued by life insurance companies require, under the Illinois Standard, full preliminary term reserves for some ages at issue and modified reserves for other ages. Thus, if the American Experience $3\frac{1}{2}\%$ Table is used, the thirty year endowment policy is valued on the full preliminary term system for ages at issue 31 and above and the twenty payment life modification is used for lower ages. For ages at issue in the vicinity of age 31, a tabulation of the net premiums and twentieth terminal reserves for this policy shows:

THIRTY YEAR ENDOWMENT
AMERICAN EXPERIENCE $3\frac{1}{2}\%$
$1000—ILLINOIS STANDARD

AGE AT ISSUE	BASIS OF RESERVES	NET PREMIUMS			TWENTIETH RESERVE
		1st	2–20	21–30	
28	20PLM	$9.11	$26.16	$24.91	$524.04
29	20PLM	8.88	26.33	25.06	524.53
30	20PLM	8.64	26.52	25.21	525.09
31	FPTM	8.22	26.47	26.47	517.07
32	FPTM	8.32	26.67	26.67	517.72
33	FPTM	8.42	26.90	26.90	518.45

The New Jersey Standard of valuation, designed to eliminate the sharp break in the sequence of values of the twentieth reserve between ages 30 and 31, divides all policies into three groups:

(a) policies with premiums greater than the twenty payment life premium at the same age;

(b) policies with premiums less than 150% of the natural premium c_x at the age at issue; and

(c) policies with premiums equal to or less than the twenty payment life premium at the same age but larger than 150% of the natural premium c_x at the age at issue.

The minimum reserves under the New Jersey Standard are as follows: for policies in group (a), reserves modified on the twenty payment life basis; for policies in group (b), reserves based upon the full preliminary term system; for policies in group (c), reserves found by a special modification similar to the full preliminary term method, but with the stipulation that the twentieth terminal reserve shall be equal to the net level reserve.

It is apparent that life and endowment policies included in group (c) are policies with premium payment periods longer than twenty years. There are net premiums of three different amounts to be considered, c_x payable in the first year, β_J payable from the second year to the twentieth year inclusive, and the net level premium P payable thereafter. Since the New Jersey Standard specifies that the modified twentieth reserve is equal to the net level reserve, it is obvious that the present value of the modified net premiums for the first twenty years may be equated to the present value of the corresponding net level premiums. Doing so, we find

$$c_x + \beta_J \cdot a_{x:\overline{19}|} = P \cdot a_{x:\overline{20}|}.$$

Solving this equation for β_J, we obtain

$$\beta_J = \frac{P \cdot a_{x:\overline{20}|} - c_x}{a_{x:\overline{19}|}},$$

and, since

$$a_{x:\overline{20}|} = 1 + a_{x:\overline{19}|},$$

it follows that

(101) $$\beta_J = P + \frac{P - c_x}{a_{x:\overline{20}|} - 1}.$$

In a manner similar to that adopted in the previous sections, we may write the prospective formulas for the net level and the modified tth terminal reserves,

$$_tV = A_{x+t:\overline{m-t}|} - P \cdot a_{x+t:\overline{n-t}|},$$

$$_tV' = A_{x+t:\overline{m-t}|} - \beta_J \cdot a_{x+t:\overline{20-t}|} - P \cdot {}_{20-t|}a_{x+t:\overline{n-20}|},$$

and, subtracting, we obtain

$$_tV - {_tV'} = (\beta_J - P)a_{x+t:\overline{20-t}|}.$$

Hence, it follows from equation (101) that

$$(102) \qquad _tV - {_tV'} = (P - c_x)\frac{a_{x+t:\overline{20-t}|}}{a_{x:\overline{20}|} - 1}.$$

It should be noted that if the value of the fraction in the right member of equation (102) is first computed, the excess of the net level reserve over the modified reserve for every value of $t < 20$ can be computed by means of the continued method described in § 40.

EXERCISES—LIST XLIII

1. Find the net premiums and the fifth terminal reserve for a $1000 thirty year endowment policy issued at age 50 modified under the New Jersey Standard. Assume that this policy is in group (c) § 58.

2. A $1000 endowment at age 60 is issued at age 20. Determine into which of the three groups this policy will fall under the New Jersey Standard and find the net premiums and tenth terminal reserve.

3. A $1000 ordinary life policy issued at age 40 lies in group (c) under the New Jersey Standard. Find the net premiums and fifth terminal reserve.

4. For a policy which falls into group (c) under the New Jersey Standard, show that

$$\beta_J = P + \frac{\beta_J - c_x}{a_{x:\overline{20}|}}.$$

59. Select and Ultimate Modification. The "Select and Ultimate" modification is a device for decreasing the first four terminal reserves for a policy, and is applied only when the American Experience Table is the basis for these reserves. The "Select and Ultimate" modification has been for many years a minimum standard for reserves in the State of New York. The underlying principle of this modification is entirely different from that involved in the modifications previously discussed in this chapter. All of these other modifications assume that the rate of mortality to be experienced by the life insurance company will follow the tabular rate. The "Select and Ultimate" method, however, recognizes that the actual rates of mortality incurred during the first five years of the policy will be, on account of selection, somewhat less than the tabular rates, and provides an arbitrary rule for determining the select rates covering this period. In the first year of insurance it is assumed that the select rate of mortality will be 50% of the tabular rate as shown by the American Experience Table for that age, in the second year 65% of the tabular rate, in the third year 75%, in the fourth year 85%, and in the fifth year 95%. A "Select and Ultimate" table, similar in form to that shown in § 6, is formed from the American Experience Table.

TERMINAL RESERVES FOR TEN YEAR ENDOWMENT

AGE AT ISSUE 30—$1000
AMERICAN EXPERIENCE $3\frac{1}{2}\%$

YEARS IN FORCE	NET LEVEL	MODIFIED F.P.T. BASIS	MODIFIED O.L. BASIS	MODIFIED [a] 20 P.L. BASIS	SELECT AND ULTIMATE
1	$ 81.98	$ 0.	$ 73.22	$ 65.56	$ 77.12
2	167.47	93.13	159.53	152.58	164.93
3	256.64	190.26	249.56	243.35	255.56
4	349.66	291.59	343.46	338.03	349.43
5	446.72	397.32	441.45	436.83	446.72
6	548.03	507.67	543.72	539.94	548.03
7	653.77	622.85	650.47	647.58	653.77
8	764.19	743.13	761.93	759.97	764.19
9	879.51	868.75	878.36	877.35	879.51
10	1000.00	1000.00	1000.00	1000.00	1000.00

[a] This set of reserves is used for this policy under both the Illinois Standard and the New Jersey Standard.

In the computation of the modified reserves both the new "Select and Ultimate" table and the original American Experience Table are used. The tth modified terminal reserve for a given policy is given by the prospective formula

$$_tV' = A_{[x]+t:\overline{m-t}|} - P \cdot a_{[x]+t:\overline{n-t}|},$$

where the net level premium P is computed from the original American Experience Table. The values of the symbols, $A_{[x]+t:\overline{m-t}|}$ and $a_{[x]+t:\overline{n-t}|}$, however, are computed from the new "Select and Ultimate" table. It is apparent, from a consideration of the two tables, that the terminal reserves on the "Select and Ultimate" basis after the fourth policy year are the usual net level reserves. The table on page 136 shows a comparison of the "Select and Ultimate" reserves with other modifications.

60. Premium Deficiency Reserves. Most states require an additional reserve in event that the gross premium for a policy is less than the net premium upon the valuation basis adopted by the company. In this event the total reserve required is the present value of future benefits less the present value of future *gross* premiums. The difference between the reserve found in this manner and the usual net premium reserve consists of the present value of the excess of the future net premiums over the gross premiums, or

$$(P - P') \cdot a_{x+t:\overline{n-t}|},$$

where P and P' are, respectively, the net and gross premiums for the given policy. This quantity is called the "premium deficiency reserve" and is maintained by the company in addition to the regular tabular net premium reserve.

As the policy grows older (as t increases) the premium deficiency reserve diminishes. It is relatively high at the shorter durations and younger ages; for example, if the gross premium on an ordinary life policy which is issued at age twenty is $1.00 less than the net premium, the premium deficiency reserve to be set up on the date of issue of the policy is $1 \cdot a_{20} = \$21.14$, on the A.E. $3\frac{1}{2}\%$ Table. It is usual for companies, in computing gross premiums, to arbitrarily make all gross premiums equal to or larger than the corresponding net premiums, thereby avoiding the necessity of maintaining large premium deficiency reserves.

The basic principles involved in the computation of gross premiums will be considered in the next chapter.

REVIEW EXERCISES—LIST XLIV

1. Fill in the missing values in the following table assuming all policies to be issued at the same age and under the same assumptions regarding mortality and interest:

POLICY	NET LEVEL PREMIUM	5TH NET LEVEL RESERVE	α_I	β_I	5TH RESERVE ILL. STD.
10 payment life	$40.61	$184.08	$24.88	$42.76	$174.19
10 yr. end.	86.68	446.72			
10 payment 15 yr. end.	74.58	377.72			
10 payment 20 yr. end.	64.93	322.71			

2. Fill in the missing values in the following table assuming all policies to be issued at the same age and under the same assumptions regarding mortality and interest:

POLICY	NET LEVEL PREMIUM	10TH NET LEVEL RESERVE	α_I	β_I	10TH RESERVE ILL. STD.
20 payment life	$24.71	$206.47	$8.14	$26.02	$195.67
20 yr. end.	39.51	395.98			
30 yr. end.	25.21	212.87			
25 yr. end.	30.69	282.98			
20 payment 30 yr. end.	31.32	291.08			

3. For an n payment policy, show that

$$\beta_O = \beta_F - \frac{\beta_F - P_{x+1}}{a_{x:\overline{n}|}}.$$

4. For an n payment policy ($n \leqq 20$), show that

(a) $$\beta_I = \beta_O + \frac{_{19}P_{x+1} - P_{x+1}}{a_{x:\overline{n}|}},$$

(b) $$\alpha_I = \alpha_O - \frac{(_{19}P_{x+1} - P_{x+1})a_{x:\overline{n-1}|}}{a_{x:\overline{n}|}}.$$

5. For a twenty year endowment policy prove that the Illinois Standard reserves will be greater than the corresponding full preliminary term reserves and less than the corresponding reserves modified on the ordinary life basis.

6. The rates of mortality at ages 30 and 31 are 0.008427 and 0.008510, respectively. Using only the table of § 59 find the net level premium and the several first year and renewal net premiums for the full preliminary term, the ordinary life modification, and the twenty payment life modification of a $1000 ten year endowment policy issued at age 30.

7. (a) Show that $\pi = 0$ for an ordinary life policy modified on the ordinary life basis, and hence the ordinary life modification of this policy is the same as the full preliminary term modification.

(b) Show that $\pi' = 0$ for a twenty payment life policy modified on the twenty payment life basis, and hence the twenty payment life modification of this policy is the same as the full preliminary term modification.

8. For a policy which falls in group (c) under the New Jersey Standard show that

$$\beta_J = {}_{19}P_{x+1} + \frac{P - {}_{20}P_x}{{}_{19}V_{x:\overline{20|}}},$$

where the symbol in the denominator denotes the nineteenth net level terminal reserve on a twenty year endowment policy issued at the same age as the policy under consideration.

9. A certain life insurance company, which is using the A.E. $3\frac{1}{2}\%$ Illinois Standard net premiums and reserves, finds that it has in force 3267 policies, for a total level amount of $5,717,250 of insurance, which fall in group (b) of § 57. Each of these policies was issued ten years ago at age 30 and provided for a premium payment period of twenty years or more. The first year net premiums for all of the policies total $75,696.39. For the entire group of policies, find:

(a) the total of the net renewal premiums;

(b) the total of the net level premiums;

(c) the total of the Illinois Standard terminal reserves;

(d) the total amount of terminal reserve needed in addition to (c) to change from the Illinois Standard to the net level system.

10. Under the ordinary life modification the difference between the net renewal modified premium and the net level premium is $1.808 for a certain $1000 policy issued at age 40. Find the length of the premium payment period.

11. For a certain thirty payment $1000 policy issued at age 40 the first year net premium modified on the F.P.T. system is $9.463, whereas the net level premium is $28.181. Find the net renewal F.P.T. premium.

12. For a certain $1000 twenty-five payment policy issued at age 50 and modified on the New Jersey Standard the renewal net premium is $42.039. Find the net level premium.

CHAPTER VI

GROSS PREMIUMS

61. Life Insurance Companies. There are two kinds of life insurance companies, stock companies and mutual companies. A stock company is one which is organized for the purpose of earning profits for the stockholders who provide the capital of the organization and who control and manage the affairs of the company. The capital of such a company forms a guarantee fund which may be drawn upon in event the premium rate charged the policyholder proves to be insufficient. A stock company usually issues *non-participating* policies, which do not provide for a distribution of the profits of the insurance, if any, to the policyholders. A mutual company is a cooperative association of policyholders established for the purpose of effecting insurance on their own lives. The profits of such a company are the property of the policyholders and the policies customarily issued provide specifically for the division of these profits. Such policies are known as *participating* policies and the profits paid to the policyholder are called *dividends*. A mutual company is controlled by its policyholders, who elect the officers and delegate to them sufficient powers to carry out the details of management.

The problem of determining an equitable scale of gross premiums for various ages and plans of insurance is of considerably more importance for non-participating policies than for participating policies. The stock company issuing non-participating policies under the stress of competition is interested in obtaining a gross premium scale as low as possible consistent with safety and conservative business judgment. The scale of premiums for participating policies, however, need not be so accurately determined, inasmuch as inequities in the scale of rates can be adjusted in the distribution of dividends. For this reason the methods of obtaining gross premiums for non-participating and participating policies will be considered separately.

62. Non-Participating Gross Premiums. The rates of interest and mortality adopted by a company for the purpose of computing non-participating gross premiums need have no relation to the minimum statutory requirements regarding net premiums and reserves. Most states require life insurance companies to maintain reserves computed according to some modified system based upon the American Experience Table of Mortality with an interest rate not greater than 4%. In contrast with these valuation requirements many companies in computing gross premiums use an interest rate in excess of 4%. Some companies use the American Men Select and Ultimate Mortality Table or a modification of this table in which the rates of mortality are chosen as percentages of those shown by the American Men Table. Thus, the gross premium charged by many companies has little relationship to the valuation net premium or to the statutory reserve, while the word "loading" implies merely the difference between two independent quantities, the gross premium and the net premium.

63. Mortality, Interest, and Expense. The first step in the preparation of a scale of non-participating gross premiums is the adoption of a table of mortality which seems likely to reflect the rate of mortality to be experienced by the company in the future. It seems fundamental, since insurance is issued only to "select" lives, that the entering policyholder should be given the benefit of the reduction in mortality due to the select class to which he belongs. The mortality table used in the formation of the gross premium scale should be a select table, showing the rate of mortality to be expected in each policy year following the date of issue. It has been argued that, in the computation of gross premiums, a company should use an ultimate rate of mortality, reflecting the mortality rate to be experienced after the effect of the selection has disappeared. The savings in mortality effected during the early policy years could then be used as an offset against the expense of selling the policy. The actual expense of selling a policy, however, bears no relation to the mortality savings resulting from the use of an ultimate table, and should properly be considered separately.

Recent mortality investigations have shown that there has been a continuous improvement in mortality at the younger ages, and the table adopted should reflect this improvement. Endowment and limited payment life policies have shown lower rates of mortality than whole life and term policies. While it may seem advisable to take account of this fluctuation in mortality reflected by the various plans of insurance, too great a refinement should be avoided because of the resulting inconvenience in computation.

The interest assumption to be used in computing the gross premium should be a conservative rate which may be expected to be earned on invested funds for many years in the future. Insurance is essentially a long-time investment and the proper choice of an interest rate is an important factor. If the rate of interest chosen is close to the rate which has been earned on similar investments in the past, it may be considered advisable to assume a reduction in the rate after a period of ten or twenty years. It is usual, however, to allow a fair margin between the assumed rate and the rate actually being earned. This margin will prove to be a source of profit and can be used to build up a substantial fund available in contingencies.

It is obvious that in the aggregate the premium income of a non-participating company should contain a sufficient allowance to pay expenses. The major problem in computing gross premiums consists in properly distributing the total expense of a company among the policies in force at various ages on the several plans of insurance. Not only do expenses vary in different companies, but different methods are used in allocating these expenses. Some of the expenses, such as agent's commissions and premium taxes, are computed directly as percentages of the gross premium. Other expenses, such as medical fees, inspection fees, collection expense, and certain clerical expenses, vary according to the number of policies considered, while expenses such as state valuation taxes are proportional to the amount of insurance in force. The clerical expense of a $100,000 policy is not as great as the corresponding expense of a hundred $1000 policies, yet the general practice is to charge the same premium rate irrespective of the size of the policy. There are legal restrictions which prohibit a company from varying the premium rate in accordance with the amount of the policy. Furthermore, the experience of life insurance companies has shown that a higher rate of mortality is to be expected in the United States under large policies than under policies of average amounts, and to a certain extent the reduced expense on a large policy can be used to offset this increased mortality.

The expense factors considered in the illustrations to follow are not in any sense to be considered as applicable to any particular company or group of companies. They are offered only for the purpose of illustrating the method of computation.

64. Computation of Gross Premiums. As an illustration of the method of computing non-participating gross premiums, consider the following example: A life insurance company estimates that the following expenses will be needed for a $1000 ten year endowment policy issued at age 35:

    (a) agent's commission, 40% of the first year gross premium and 3% of each gross premium thereafter;

    (b) premium taxes, 3% of each gross premium; and

    (c) administrative expense, $3.00 in the first year, and $1.00 per year thereafter.

It is customary for life insurance companies to pay the face amount of insurance immediately upon receipt of proof of the death of the insured. All of the formulas derived in the previous chapters have been based upon the assumption that death claims are payable at the end of the year in which the insured dies. Since on the average the date of death will fall in the middle of the policy year, it is necessary to add a half-year's interest to the face amount of insurance when these formulas are used for the purpose of computing gross premiums.

Let us assume that the life insurance company issuing the above policy adopts the American Men Select and Ultimate Mortality Table with interest at $4\frac{1}{2}\%$ as a basis for its gross premium computations. It is obvious that the present value of all gross premiums to be received by the company for this policy must at least be sufficient to cover the present value of the estimated expenses and benefits provided. If one denotes by P' this minimum gross premium for the ten year endowment policy under consideration, then P' is determined by equating the present value of the gross premiums to the present value of the benefits plus the present value of the estimated expenses. Hence we write the equation

(103) $P' a_{[35]:\overline{10|}} = 1000\,[(1.0225) \cdot A^1_{[35]:\overline{10|}} + {}_{10}E_{[35]}] + 3$

$\qquad\qquad + 1 \cdot a_{[35]:\overline{9|}} + P'\,[0.4 + 0.03a_{[35]:\overline{9|}} + 0.03a_{[35]:\overline{10|}}],$

where the bracket enclosing the age [35] is used to indicate
that the life under discussion is a select life at age 35. In
using select tables it should be noted that the value of a
given symbol depends not only upon the attained age of
the insured, but also upon the age at which the policy was
issued. In general, the symbol $[x] + t$ indicates a life, now
aged $x + t$, who was accepted for insurance t years ago at
age x. After the select period expires, all lives of the same
attained age are considered to be subject to the same ultimate rate of mortality and the bracket enclosing the age
at issue is dropped. In the present instance the bracket
is omitted after the insured reaches age 40, inasmuch as the
select period of the American Men Table extends for only
five years.

Solving equation (103) for the gross premium P', we may
write

$$P' = \frac{1022.5A^1_{[35]:\overline{10|}} + 1000\,{}_{10}E_{[35]} + 3 + a_{[35]:\overline{9|}}}{a_{[35]:\overline{10|}} - [0.4 + 0.03a_{[35]:\overline{9|}} + 0.03a_{[35]:\overline{10|}}]},$$

which, upon inserting commutation symbols and simplifying, becomes

(104)

$$P' = \frac{(1022.5)(M_{[35]} - M_{45}) + 1000D_{45} + 3D_{[35]} + N_{[35]+1} - N_{45}}{0.57N_{[35]} + 0.37N_{[35]+1} - 0.94N_{45}},$$

where the symbol $[35] + 1$ indicates a life aged 36 who was a
select life one year previously at age 35. Equation (104) gives

$$P' = 91.211$$

after a computation which makes use of the table of values
appearing below.

The following table shows the values of some of the symbols

based on the American Men Select and Ultimate Table with interest at $4\frac{1}{2}\%$.

COMMUTATION VALUES		ACCUMULATION FACTORS		
		t	$u_{[35]+t}$	$(1022.5) \cdot k_{[35]+t}$
$N_{[35]}$	336018.8	0	1.048317	3.24543
$N_{[35]+1}$	316380.9	1	1.049503	4.40583
N_{45}	176722.8	2	1.049800	4.69705
N_{55}	81654.26	3	1.050044	4.93528
$D_{[35]}$	19637.92	4	1.050490	5.37180
D_{45}	11967.31	5	1.051144	6.01140
D_{55}	6865.306	6	1.051476	6.33724
$M_{[35]}$	5168.208	7	1.051876	6.72750
M_{45}	4357.234	8	1.052306	7.14896
M_{55}	3349.094	9	1.052806	7.63851

EXERCISES—LIST XLV

1. It is estimated that the following expenses are required for a $1000 ten year term policy issued at age 35:

(a) commission, 40% of gross premium in the first year and 5% thereafter;

(b) premium taxes, 2% of each gross premium; and

(c) administrative expense, $2.50 the first year and $2.00 in each succeeding year.

Using the commutation symbols of § 64, compute the minimum gross premium for this policy.

2. A life insurance company estimates that the following expenses are required for a $1000 ten year endowment policy issued at age 35:

(a) commission, 35% of the first year gross premium and 5% thereafter;

(b) premium taxes, 3% of each gross premium; and

(c) administrative expense, $3.50 in the first year and $1.50 in each succeeding year.

Using the commutation symbols of § 64, compute the minimum gross premium for this policy.

3. It is estimated that the following expenses will be incurred on a $1000 twenty payment life policy issued at age 35:

(a) commission, 60% of the first year gross premium and 5% thereafter;

(b) premium tax, 3% of each gross premium; and

(c) administrative expense, $4.50 in the first year and $2.00 in each succeeding year until the death of the policyholder.

(1) Using the commutation symbols of § 64 compute the minimum gross premium for this policy.

(2) If the net premium is $28.89, what premium deficiency reserve must be maintained at the end of the fifth policy year? Use the A.E. $3\frac{1}{2}$% Table in this computation.

65. Asset Shares. In § 64 the minimum gross premium P' for a $1000 ten year endowment policy issued at age 35 was found to be $91.21 under certain assumptions regarding mortality, interest, and expense. Assume that the company maintains legal reserves based upon the Illinois Standard system of modification and the American Experience $3\frac{1}{2}$% Table. Since the gross premium is not based on the same mortality table and interest rate as the net premium and terminal reserves, an additional investigation is required to disclose whether this gross premium is sufficient to meet the legal requirements for surrender values.

The expenses to be paid by the company in the first year of the ten year endowment policy amount to $3.00 plus 43% of the gross premium, a total of $42.221. The deduction of this amount from the gross premium leaves a balance, called the *effective* premium, of $48.990. When the effective premium is accumulated with benefit of interest and survivorship and the accumulated cost of insurance is deducted, one obtains (using the values shown in § 64)

$$48.990u_{[35]} - (1022.5)k_{[35]} = (48.990)(1.048317) - 3.24543$$
$$= 48.112.$$

This amount, $48.112, which represents the accumulated excess of the gross premium over expenses and cost of insurance, is called the *asset share*, or *natural reserve*, at the end of the first policy year.

The expenses to be paid by the company in the second policy year amount to $1.00 plus 6% of the gross premium, a total of $6.473. The effective premium for this year is $84.738, and the second asset share is

$$(48.112 + 84.738)(1.049503) - 4.40583 = 135.021.$$

This procedure is repeated until all of the ten asset shares for the policy have been computed. A comparison of the asset shares with the corresponding American Experience $3\frac{1}{2}\%$ Illinois Standard terminal reserves shows:

COMPARISON OF ASSET SHARES AND ILLINOIS STANDARD
RESERVES

TEN YEAR ENDOWMENT   GROSS PREMIUM $91.211   AGE AT ISSUE 35

End of Year	NET PREMIUMS ILLINOIS STANDARD 1ST YEAR $69.22 RENEWAL 89.47	EFFECTIVE PREMIUMS 1ST YEAR $48.99 RENEWAL 84.74	
	Terminal Reserve Illinois Standard Amer. Exp. $3\frac{1}{2}\%$	Asset Share A.M.S. & U. $4\frac{1}{2}\%$	Difference
1	$ 63.26	$ 48.11	$15.15
2	150.35	135.02	15.33
3	241.20	226.01	15.19
4	335.99	321.36	14.63
5	434.93	421.23	13.70
6	538.23	525.83	12.40
7	646.12	635.66	10.46
8	758.86	751.05	7.81
9	876.72	872.35	4.37
10	1000.00	1000.00	0.

The table shows that the terminal reserve exceeds the asset share in every year except the last, when the two are equal.

In § 42 it was stated that surrender values are customarily based upon the legal reserve less a surrender charge, which in most states cannot exceed $25 per $1000 of insurance. An examination of the above table will show what charge can reasonably be made. The cash surrender value to be allowed at the end of any policy year should be not greater than the actual accumulation as shown by the asset share column. Hence, the differences shown in the last column of the table are the minimum surrender charges which can be used by the company in computing the surrender options. Inasmuch as these differences never exceed $25.00, the maximum legal charge, it is evident that in this illustration the minimum gross premium is adequate to meet the legal requirements for cash values.

Since the method of § 64 makes no allowance for profit to the insurance company, it is common practice to adopt a gross premium which is slightly higher than the calculated minimum premium P'. The asset shares based upon this increased premium will be higher than the asset shares shown in the table and will exceed the legal reserve before the maturity of the policy. There are different practices in common use varying the length of time which elapses before the asset share becomes greater than the legal reserve. An investigation of the gross premiums charged by several companies shows that this period varies from as low as four or five years in the case of short term endowment policies to fifteen or twenty years in the case of whole life policies.*

EXERCISES—LIST XLVI

1. A certain life insurance company charges a gross premium of $21.10 for a $1000 ordinary life policy issued at age 35. The expenses incurred by this policy amount to $15.46 the first year and $3.75 in each renewal year. (a) On the basis of the American Men Select and Ultimate $4\frac{1}{2}\%$ Table, compute the first five asset shares. (b) If the

* For further reading in the subject of non-participating gross premiums, the student is referred to E. E. Cammack, *Premiums for non-participating life insurances*, Transactions of the Actuarial Society of America, vol. 20 (1919), pp. 379–409 and W. A. Jenkins, *Non-participating premiums considering withdrawals*, Record of the American Institute of Actuaries, vol. 21 (1932), pp. 8–22.

third legal reserve is \$36.45, what is the minimum surrender charge which can be made at the end of the third policy year?

2. A certain life insurance company charges a gross premium of \$42.00 for a \$1000 twenty year endowment policy issued at age 35. The expenses incurred by this policy amount to \$18.36 the first year and \$3.00 in each renewal year. (a) On the basis of the American Men Select and Ultimate $4\frac{1}{2}\%$ Table, compute the first five asset shares. (b) If the fifth legal reserve is \$188.18, what is the minimum surrender charge which can be made at the end of the fifth policy year?

66. Participating Gross Premiums.

It is not necessary to compute with great accuracy the gross premium for a participating policy, since it is expected that a part of the premium will be refunded to the policyholder in the form of dividends. It is only necessary that the gross premium scale be sufficient to care for all fluctuations in mortality, interest, and expense that might occur. Minor inequities in the scale of gross premiums can be adjusted in the distribution of dividends. The method of determining participating gross premiums varies with different companies. Many life insurance companies compute the gross premium for a given policy by adding a constant to the net level premium and multiplying the sum by a percentage factor. Thus, if P' denotes the gross premium, this method implies that

$$(105) \qquad P' = (P + c)(1 + k),$$

where c and k are constants and P denotes the net level premium for the policy under consideration. It is customary, in applying equation (105), to vary the values of c and k with the plan of insurance.

EXERCISES—LIST XLVII

1. A single premium whole life policy is sold at age 25 with the provision that the gross premium without interest will be returned, together with the face amount \$1000, at the death of the insured. Assuming the gross premium is obtained by the method of equation (105), with $c = \$5$ for a \$1000 policy and $k = .1$, compute the net and gross premiums for this policy.

SOLUTION. Denote the net premium by W and the gross premium by W'. Since the net premium W must be sufficient to provide whole life insurance of $(1000 + W')$, we have immediately

$$W = (1000 + W')A_{25}.$$

Equation (105) implies that

$$W' = (W + 5)(1.1).$$

Solving these two equations simultaneously for W, we get, by Table IV,

$$W = \frac{1005.5A_{25}}{1 - 1.1A_{25}} = \frac{(1005.5)(0.3087342)}{1 - (1.1)(0.3087342)} = \$470.07,$$

and hence

$$W' = (W + 5)(1.1) = \$522.58.$$

2. An ordinary life policy is issued at age 30 with the provision that the gross premiums paid by the insured will be returned without interest, together with the face amount \$1000, at the death of the insured. Assuming that the gross premium is obtained by the method of equation (105), with $c = \$4$ for a \$1000 policy and $k = 0.07$, compute the net and gross premiums for the policy.

3. A formula, used in England, for loading the net level annual premium for an ordinary life policy is

$$P'_x = 1.075\left[P_x + \frac{0.01}{a_x} + 0.00125 \right].$$

Show that this method is equivalent to that of equation (105) and find the values of c and k corresponding to an interest rate of $3\frac{1}{2}\%$.

4. A twenty payment life policy is issued at age 30 with the provision that the gross premiums paid by the insured will be returned without interest, together with the face amount \$1000, at the death of the insured. Assuming that the gross premium is obtained by the method of equation (105), with $c = 0.005$ and $k = 0.09$, show that

(a) the net premium for this policy is

$$\frac{1000M_{30} + 5.45(R_{30} - R_{50})}{N_{30} - N_{50} - 1.09(R_{30} - R_{50})};$$

(b) the gross premium for this policy is

$$1.09\frac{1000M_{30} + 5(N_{30} - N_{50})}{N_{30} - N_{50} - 1.09(R_{30} - R_{50})}.$$

TABLES

AMERICAN EXPERIENCE 3½%

Table I — Accumulation and Discount Factors

$3\frac{1}{2}\%$ Interest

n	$(1.035)^{n}$	$(1.035)^{-n}$	$s_{\overline{n}\rvert}$	$a_{\overline{n}\rvert}$	$1/a_{\overline{n}\rvert}$	n
1	1.035000	0.9661836	1.000000	0.9661836	1.035000	1
2	1.071225	0.9335107	2.035000	1.8996943	0.526400	2
3	1.108718	0.9019427	3.106225	2.8016370	0.356934	3
4	1.147523	0.8714422	4.214943	3.6730792	0.272251	4
5	1.187686	0.8419732	5.362466	4.5150524	0.221481	5
6	1.229255	0.8135006	6.550152	5.3285530	0.187668	6
7	1.272279	0.7859910	7.779408	6.1145440	0.163544	7
8	1.316809	0.7594116	9.051687	6.8739555	0.145477	8
9	1.362897	0.7337310	10.368496	7.6076865	0.131446	9
10	1.410599	0.7089188	11.731393	8.3166053	0.120241	10
11	1.459970	0.6849457	13.141992	9.0015510	0.111092	11
12	1.511069	0.6617833	14.601962	9.6633343	0.103484	12
13	1.563956	0.6394042	16.113030	10.3027385	0.097062	13
14	1.618695	0.6177818	17.676986	10.9205203	0.091571	14
15	1.675349	0.5968906	19.295681	11.5174109	0.086825	15
16	1.733986	0.5767059	20.971030	12.0941168	0.082685	16
17	1.794676	0.5572038	22.705016	12.6513206	0.079043	17
18	1.857489	0.5383611	24.499691	13.1896817	0.075817	18
19	1.922501	0.5201557	26.357180	13.7098374	0.072940	19
20	1.989789	0.5025659	28.279682	14.2124033	0.070361	20
21	2.059431	0.4855709	30.269471	14.6979742	0.068037	21
22	2.131512	0.4691506	32.328902	15.1671248	0.065932	22
23	2.206114	0.4532856	34.460414	15.6204105	0.064019	23
24	2.283328	0.4379571	36.666528	16.0583676	0.062273	24
25	2.363245	0.4231470	38.949857	16.4815146	0.060674	25
26	2.445959	0.4088377	41.313102	16.8903523	0.059205	26
27	2.531567	0.3950122	43.759060	17.2853645	0.057852	27
28	2.620172	0.3816543	46.290627	17.6670188	0.056603	28
29	2.711878	0.3687482	48.910799	18.0357670	0.055445	29
30	2.806794	0.3562784	51.622677	18.3920454	0.054371	30
31	2.905031	0.3442304	54.429471	18.7362758	0.053372	31
32	3.006708	0.3325897	57.334502	19.0688655	0.052442	32
33	3.111942	0.3213427	60.341210	19.3902082	0.051572	33
34	3.220860	0.3104760	63.453152	19.7006842	0.050760	34
35	3.333590	0.2999769	66.674013	20.0006611	0.049998	35
36	3.450266	0.2898327	70.007603	20.2904938	0.049284	36
37	3.571025	0.2800316	73.457869	20.5705254	0.048613	37
38	3.696011	0.2705619	77.028895	20.8410874	0.047982	38
39	3.825372	0.2614125	80.724906	21.1024999	0.047388	39
40	3.959260	0.2525725	84.550278	21.3550723	0.046827	40
41	4.097834	0.2440314	88.509537	21.5991037	0.046298	41
42	4.241258	0.2357791	92.607371	21.8348828	0.045798	42
43	4.389702	0.2278059	96.848629	22.0626887	0.045325	43
44	4.543342	0.2201023	101.238331	22.2827910	0.044878	44
45	4.702359	0.2126592	105.781673	22.4954503	0.044453	45
46	4.866941	0.2054679	110.484031	22.7009181	0.044051	46
47	5.037284	0.1985197	115.350973	22.8994378	0.043669	47
48	5.213589	0.1918064	120.388257	23.0912442	0.043306	48
49	5.396065	0.1853202	125.601846	23.2765645	0.042962	49
50	5.584927	0.1790534	130.997910	23.4556179	0.042634	50

Table I (*Continued*) — Accumulation and Discount Factors

3½% Interest

n	$(1.035)^n$	$(1.035)^{-n}$	$s_{\overline{n}\rvert}$	$a_{\overline{n}\rvert}$	$1/a_{\overline{n}\rvert}$	n
51	5.780399	0.1729984	136.582837	23.6286163	0.042322	51
52	5.982713	0.1671482	142.363236	23.7957645	0.042024	52
53	6.192108	0.1614959	148.345950	23.9572604	0.041741	53
54	6.408832	0.1560347	154.538058	24.1132951	0.041471	54
55	6.633141	0.1507581	160.946890	24.2640532	0.041213	55
56	6.865301	0.1456600	167.580031	24.4097133	0.040967	56
57	7.105587	0.1407343	174.445332	24.5504476	0.040732	57
58	7.354282	0.1359752	181.550919	24.6864228	0.040508	58
59	7.611682	0.1313770	188.905201	24.8177998	0.040294	59
60	7.878091	0.1269343	196.516883	24.9447341	0.040089	60
61	8.153824	0.1226418	204.394974	25.0673760	0.039892	61
62	8.439208	0.1184945	212.548798	25.1858705	0.039705	62
63	8.734580	0.1144875	220.988006	25.3003580	0.039525	63
64	9.040291	0.1106159	229.722586	25.4109739	0.039353	64
65	9.356701	0.1068753	238.762876	25.5178492	0.039188	65
66	9.684185	0.1032611	248.119577	25.6211103	0.039030	66
67	10.023132	0.0997692	257.803762	25.7208795	0.038879	67
68	10.373941	0.0963954	267.826894	25.8172749	0.038734	68
69	10.737029	0.0931356	278.200835	25.9104105	0.038595	69
70	11.112825	0.0899861	288.937865	26.0003966	0.038461	70
71	11.501774	0.0869431	300.050690	26.0873398	0.038333	71
72	11.904336	0.0840030	311.552464	26.1713428	0.038210	72
73	12.320988	0.0811623	323.456800	26.2525051	0.038092	73
74	12.752223	0.0784177	335.777788	26.3309228	0.037978	74
75	13.198550	0.0757659	348.530011	26.4066887	0.037869	75
76	13.660500	0.0732038	361.728561	26.4798924	0.037764	76
77	14.138617	0.0707283	375.389061	26.5506207	0.037664	77
78	14.633469	0.0683365	389.527678	26.6189572	0.037567	78
79	15.145640	0.0660256	404.161147	26.6849828	0.037474	79
80	15.675738	0.0637928	419.306787	26.7487757	0.037385	80
81	16.224388	0.0616356	434.982524	26.8104113	0.037299	81
82	16.792242	0.0595513	451.206913	26.8699626	0.037216	82
83	17.379970	0.0575375	467.999155	26.9275001	0.037137	83
84	17.988269	0.0555918	485.379125	26.9830919	0.037060	84
85	18.617859	0.0537119	503.367394	27.0368037	0.036987	85
86	19.269484	0.0518955	521.985253	27.0886993	0.036916	86
87	19.943916	0.0501406	541.254737	27.1388399	0.036848	87
88	20.641953	0.0484450	561.198653	27.1872849	0.036782	88
89	21.364421	0.0468068	581.840606	27.2340917	0.036719	89
90	22.112176	0.0452240	603.205027	27.2793156	0.036658	90
91	22.886102	0.0436946	625.317203	27.3230103	0.036599	91
92	23.687116	0.0422170	648.203305	27.3652273	0.036543	92
93	24.516165	0.0407894	671.890421	27.4060167	0.036488	93
94	25.374230	0.0394101	696.406585	27.4454268	0.036436	94
95	26.262329	0.0380774	721.780816	27.4835042	0.036385	95
96	27.181510	0.0367897	748.043145	27.5202939	0.036337	96
97	28.132863	0.0355456	775.224655	27.5558395	0.036290	97
98	29.117513	0.0343436	803.357517	27.5901831	0.036245	98
99	30.136626	0.0331822	832.475031	27.6233653	0.036201	99
100	31.191408	0.0320601	862.611657	27.6554254	0.036159	100

155

Table II — American Experience Table of Mortality

x	l_x	d_x	q_x	$\overset{\circ}{e}_x$	x
10	100000	749	.007490	48.72	10
11	99251	746	.007516	48.08	11
12	98505	743	.007543	47.45	12
13	97762	740	.007569	46.80	13
14	97022	737	.007596	46.16	14
15	96285	735	.007634	45.50	15
16	95550	732	.007661	44.85	16
17	94818	729	.007688	44.19	17
18	94089	727	.007727	43.53	18
19	93362	725	.007765	42.87	19
20	92637	723	.007805	42.20	20
21	91914	722	.007855	41.53	21
22	91192	721	.007906	40.85	22
23	90471	720	.007958	40.17	23
24	89751	719	.008011	39.49	24
25	89032	718	.008065	38.81	25
26	88314	718	.008130	38.12	26
27	87596	718	.008197	37.43	27
28	86878	718	.008264	36.73	28
29	86160	719	.008345	36.03	29
30	85441	720	.008427	35.33	30
31	84721	721	.008510	34.63	31
32	84000	723	.008607	33.92	32
33	83277	726	.008718	33.21	33
34	82551	729	.008831	32.50	34
35	81822	732	.008946	31.78	35
36	81090	737	.009089	31.07	36
37	80353	742	.009234	30.35	37
38	79611	749	.009408	29.62	38
39	78862	756	.009586	28.90	39
40	78106	765	.009794	28.18	40
41	77341	774	.010008	27.45	41
42	76567	785	.010252	26.72	42
43	75782	797	.010517	26.00	43
44	74985	812	.010829	25.27	44
45	74173	828	.011163	24.54	45
46	73345	848	.011562	23.81	46
47	72497	870	.012000	23.08	47
48	71627	896	.012509	22.36	48
49	70731	927	.013106	21.63	49
50	69804	962	.013781	20.91	50
51	68842	1001	.014541	20.20	51
52	67841	1044	.015389	19.49	52
53	66797	1091	.016333	18.79	53
54	65706	1143	.017396	18.09	54

Table II (*Continued*) — American Experience Table of Mortality

x	l_x	d_x	q_x	$\overset{\circ}{e}_x$	x
55	64563	1199	.018571	17.40	55
56	63364	1260	.019885	16.72	56
57	62104	1325	.021335	16.05	57
58	60779	1394	.022936	15.39	58
59	59385	1468	.024720	14.74	59
60	57917	1546	.026693	14.10	60
61	56371	1628	.028880	13.47	61
62	54743	1713	.031292	12.86	62
63	53030	1800	.033943	12.26	63
64	51230	1889	.036873	11.67	64
65	49341	1980	.040129	11.10	65
66	47361	2070	.043707	10.54	66
67	45291	2158	.047647	10.00	67
68	43133	2243	.052002	9.47	68
69	40890	2321	.056762	8.97	69
70	38569	2391	.061993	8.48	70
71	36178	2448	.067665	8.00	71
72	33730	2487	.073733	7.55	72
73	31243	2505	.080178	7.11	73
74	28738	2501	.087028	6.68	74
75	26237	2476	.094371	6.27	75
76	23761	2431	.102311	5.88	76
77	21330	2369	.111064	5.49	77
78	18961	2291	.120827	5.11	78
79	16670	2196	.131734	4.74	79
80	14474	2091	.144466	4.39	80
81	12383	1964	.158605	4.05	81
82	10419	1816	.174297	3.71	82
83	8603	1648	.191561	3.39	83
84	6955	1470	.211359	3.08	84
85	5485	1292	.235552	2.77	85
86	4193	1114	.265681	2.47	86
87	3079	933	.303020	2.18	87
88	2146	744	.346692	1.91	88
89	1402	555	.395863	1.66	89
90	847	385	.454545	1.42	90
91	462	246	.532468	1.19	91
92	216	137	.634259	.98	92
93	79	58	.734177	.80	93
94	21	18	.857143	.64	94
95	3	3	1.000000	.50	95
96	0				96

Table III — American Experience 3½%

Commutation Columns

x	D_x	N_x	S_x	C_x	M_x	R_x	x
15	57471.613	1249025.0	23055464.	423.87885	15234.051	469371.67	15
16	55104.250	1191553.4	21806439.	407.87317	14810.172	454137.61	16
17	52832.948	1136449.2	20614886.	392.46527	14402.299	439327.44	17
18	50653.861	1083616.2	19478437.	378.15319	14009.834	424925.14	18
19	48562.776	1032962.4	18394820.	364.36027	13631.681	410915.31	19
20	46556.196	984399.60	17361858.	351.06776	13267.321	397283.63	20
21	44630.764	937843.40	16377458.	338.72676	12916.253	384016.31	21
22	42782.784	893212.64	15439615.	326.81894	12577.526	371100.05	22
23	41009.205	850429.85	14546402.	315.32914	12250.707	358522.53	23
24	39307.091	809420.65	13695972.	304.24269	11935.378	346271.82	24
25	37673.623	770113.56	12886552.	293.54545	11631.135	334336.44	25
26	36106.090	732439.93	12116438.	283.61879	11337.590	322705.31	26
27	34601.492	696333.84	11383998.	274.02782	11053.971	311367.72	27
28	33157.366	661732.35	10687664.	264.76118	10779.943	300313.75	28
29	31771.341	628574.99	10025932.	256.16418	10515.182	289533.80	29
30	30440.784	596803.64	9397357.1	247.84585	10259.018	279018.62	30
31	29163.539	566362.86	8800553.5	239.79718	10011.172	268759.60	31
32	27937.536	537199.32	8234190.6	232.33078	9771.3749	258748.43	32
33	26760.457	509261.79	7696991.3	225.40561	9539.0441	248977.06	33
34	25630.109	482501.33	7187729.5	218.68313	9313.6385	239438.01	34
35	24544.707	456871.22	6705228.2	212.15755	9094.9554	230124.37	35
36	23502.535	432326.51	6248356.9	206.38330	8882.7978	221029.42	36
37	22501.380	408823.98	5816030.4	200.75696	8676.4145	212146.62	37
38	21539.707	386322.60	5407206.4	195.79797	8475.6576	203470.21	38
39	20615.513	364782.89	5020883.8	190.94479	8279.8596	194994.55	39
40	19727.425	344167.38	4656101.0	186.68400	8088.9148	186714.69	40
41	18873.630	324439.95	4311933.6	182.49302	7902.2308	178625.77	41
42	18052.898	305566.32	3987493.6	178.82763	7719.7378	170723.54	42
43	17263.586	287513.42	3681927.3	175.42154	7540.9102	163003.81	43
44	16504.372	270249.84	3394413.9	172.67930	7365.4886	155462.90	44
45	15773.574	253745.47	3124164.0	170.12739	7192.8093	148097.41	45
46	15070.041	237971.89	2870418.6	168.34469	7022.6819	140904.60	46
47	14392.081	222901.85	2632446.7	166.87161	6854.3372	133881.92	47
48	13738.521	208509.77	2409544.8	166.04694	6687.4656	127027.58	48
49	13107.886	194771.25	2201035.1	165.98248	6521.4187	120340.11	49
50	12498.642	181663.36	2006263.8	166.42449	6355.4362	113818.69	50
51	11909.558	169164.72	1824600.4	167.31539	6189.0117	107463.26	51
52	11339.504	157255.16	1655435.7	168.60170	6021.6963	101274.25	52
53	10787.441	145915.66	1498180.6	170.23383	5853.0946	95252.550	53
54	10252.414	135128.22	1352264.9	172.31655	5682.8608	89399.456	54

Table III (*Continued*) — American Experience $3\frac{1}{2}\%$

Commutation Columns

x	D_x	N_x	S_x	C_x	M_x	R_x	x
55	9733.3976	124875.81	1217136.7	174.64638	5510.5442	83716.595	55
56	9229.6025	115142.41	1092260.9	177.32526	5335.8979	78206.051	56
57	8740.1651	105912.81	977118.46	180.16714	5158.5726	72870.153	57
58	8264.4368	97172.641	871205.65	183.13955	4978.4055	67711.580	58
59	7801.8235	88908.204	774033.01	186.33956	4795.2659	62733.175	59
60	7351.6542	81106.381	685124.81	189.60429	4608.9263	57937.909	60
61	6913.4432	73754.726	604018.43	192.90910	4419.3221	53328.982	61
62	6486.7462	66841.283	530263.70	196.11704	4226.4130	48909.660	62
63	6071.2706	60354.537	463422.42	199.10865	4030.2959	44683.247	63
64	5666.8533	54283.266	403067.88	201.88740	3831.1873	40652.951	64
65	5273.3332	48616.413	348784.61	204.45706	3629.2999	36821.764	65
66	4890.5508	43343.080	300168.20	206.52228	3424.8428	33192.464	66
67	4518.6476	38452.529	256825.12	208.02123	3218.3205	29767.621	67
68	4157.8219	33933.881	218372.59	208.90322	3010.2993	26549.301	68
69	3808.3160	29776.060	184438.71	208.85778	2801.3961	23539.002	69
70	3470.6746	25967.744	154662.65	207.88097	2592.5383	20737.606	70
71	3145.4278	22497.069	128694.91	205.63935	2384.6573	18145.067	71
72	2833.4213	19351.641	106197.84	201.85070	2179.0180	15760.410	72
73	2535.7544	16518.220	86846.198	196.43635	1977.1673	13581.392	73
74	2253.5679	13982.465	70327.978	189.49051	1780.7309	11604.225	74
75	1987.8698	11728.897	56345.513	181.25252	1591.2404	9823.4937	75
76	1739.3946	9741.0277	44616.615	171.94044	1409.9879	8232.2532	76
77	1508.6341	8001.6330	34875.588	161.88916	1238.0475	6822.2653	77
78	1295.7283	6492.9989	26873.955	151.26465	1076.1583	5584.2178	78
79	1100.6468	5197.2706	20380.956	140.08910	924.89367	4508.0595	79
80	923.33774	4096.6238	15183.685	128.88005	784.80456	3583.1658	80
81	763.23370	3173.2861	11087.061	116.95877	655.92451	2798.3613	81
82	620.46510	2410.0524	7913.7754	104.48810	538.96574	2142.4368	82
83	494.99509	1789.5873	5503.7230	91.615261	434.47764	1603.4710	83
84	386.64086	1294.5922	3714.1358	78.956448	342.86238	1168.9934	84
85	294.60960	907.95132	2419.5436	67.049020	263.90594	826.13101	85
86	217.59794	613.34172	1511.5922	55.856634	196.85692	562.22507	86
87	154.38292	395.74378	898.25053	45.199212	141.00028	365.36815	87
88	103.96303	241.36085	502.50676	34.824253	95.801071	224.36787	88
89	65.623121	137.39782	261.14591	25.099294	60.976818	128.56680	89
90	38.304688	71.774700	123.74808	16.822437	35.877524	67.589983	90
91	20.186924	33.470012	51.973383	10.385393	19.055088	31.712458	91
92	9.1188815	13.283089	18.503371	5.5881498	8.6696949	12.657371	92
93	3.2223637	4.1642071	5.2202825	2.2857836	3.0815451	3.9876758	93
94	.82761130	.94184337	1.0560754	.68539238	.79576153	.90613067	94
95	.11423206	.11423206	.11423206	.11036914	.11036914	.11036914	95

159

Table IV — Life Annuity Due, Single Premium and Reciprocals

x	a_x	$-\Delta a_x{}^*$	$1000/a_x$	$1000A_x$	$1/A_x$	x
15	21.732904	.109283	46.01318	265.0709	3.772576	15
16	21.623621	.113385	46.24572	268.7664	3.720703	16
17	21.510236	.117667	46.48949	272.6007	3.668369	17
18	21.392569	.121907	46.74520	276.5798	3.615593	18
19	21.270662	.126331	47.01311	280.7023	3.562494	19
20	21.144331	.130947	47.29400	284.9743	3.509088	20
21	21.013384	.135532	47.58872	289.4025	3.455396	21
22	20.877852	.140316	47.89765	293.9857	3.401526	22
23	20.737536	.145306	48.22174	298.7307	3.347497	23
24	20.592230	.150512	48.56201	303.6444	3.293326	24
25	20.441718	.155945	48.91957	308.7342	3.239032	25
26	20.285773	.161385	49.29563	314.0077	3.184635	26
27	20.124388	.167062	49.69095	319.4652	3.130232	27
28	19.957326	.172987	50.10691	325.1146	3.075839	28
29	19.784339	.178942	50.54503	330.9644	3.021473	29
30	19.605397	.185159	51.00636	337.0156	2.967222	30
31	19.420238	.191651	51.49268	343.2770	2.913099	31
32	19.228587	.198203	52.00590	349.7579	2.859120	32
33	19.030384	.204817	52.54755	356.4604	2.805360	33
34	18.825567	.211728	53.11925	363.3866	2.751890	34
35	18.613839	.218950	53.72347	370.5465	2.698717	35
36	18.394889	.226049	54.36293	377.9506	2.645848	36
37	18.168840	.233471	55.03929	385.5948	2.593396	37
38	17.935369	.240787	55.75575	393.4899	2.541361	38
39	17.694582	.248444	56.51447	401.6325	2.489838	39
40	17.446138	.256019	57.31928	410.0340	2.438822	40
41	17.190119	.263955	58.17295	418.6916	2.388393	41
42	16.926164	.271836	59.08013	427.6176	2.338538	42
43	16.654328	.279889	60.04445	436.8102	2.289324	43
44	16.374439	.287694	61.07079	446.2750	2.240771	44
45	16.086745	.295687	62.16298	456.0038	2.192964	45
46	15.791058	.303246	63.32698	466.0029	2.145910	46
47	15.487812	.310794	64.56690	476.2575	2.099704	47
48	15.177018	.317929	65.88910	486.7675	2.054369	48
49	14.859089	.324441	67.29888	497.5187	2.009975	49
50	14.534648	.330534	68.80111	508.4901	1.966606	50
51	14.204114	.336209	70.40214	519.6676	1.924307	51
52	13.867905	.341466	72.10894	531.0370	1.883108	52
53	13.526439	.346302	73.92929	542.5842	1.843032	53
54	13.180137	.350516	75.87175	554.2949	1.804094	54

$^* - \Delta a_x = a_x - a_{x+1}.$

Table IV (*Continued*) — Life Annuity Due, Single Premium and Reciprocals

3½%   d = .0338 1643   American Experience

x	a_x	$-\Delta a_x^*$	$1000/a_x$	$1000A_x$	$1/A_x$	x
55	12.829621	.354283	77.94462	566.1481	1.766322	55
56	12.475338	.357397	80.15815	578.1287	1.729719	56
57	12.117941	.360014	82.52227	590.2146	1.694299	57
58	11.757927	.362103	85.04901	602.3890	1.660057	58
59	11.395824	.363425	87.75145	614.6340	1.626985	59
60	11.032399	.364093	90.64212	626.9237	1.595090	60
61	10.668306	.364021	93.73560	639.2360	1.564367	61
62	10.304285	.363279	97.04700	651.5459	1.534811	62
63	9.941006	.361922	100.5934	663.8307	1.506408	63
64	9.579084	.359789	104.3941	676.0696	1.479138	64
65	9.219295	.356678	108.4682	688.2364	1.452989	65
66	8.862617	.352874	112.8335	700.2980	1.427964	66
67	8.509743	.348287	117.5124	712.2309	1.404039	67
68	8.161456	.342761	122.5272	724.0087	1.381199	68
69	7.818695	.336650	127.8986	735.5997	1.359435	69
70	7.482045	.329737	133.6533	746.9840	1.338717	70
71	7.152308	.322529	139.8150	758.1345	1.319027	71
72	6.829779	.315655	146.4176	769.0413	1.300320	72
73	6.514124	.309534	153.5126	779.7156	1.282519	73
74	6.204590	.304356	161.1710	790.1830	1.265530	74
75	5.900234	.299994	169.4848	800.4751	1.249258	75
76	5.600240	.296348	178.5638	810.6200	1.233624	76
77	5.303892	.292812	188.5408	820.6414	1.218559	77
78	5.011080	.289065	199.5578	830.5432	1.204031	78
79	4.722015	.285259	211.7740	840.3184	1.190025	79
80	4.436756	.279070	225.3899	849.9649	1.176519	80
81	4.157686	.273419	240.5184	859.4019	1.163600	81
82	3.884267	.268903	257.4488	868.6480	1.151214	82
83	3.615364	.267057	276.5973	877.7413	1.139288	83
84	3.348307	.266427	298.6584	886.7722	1.127685	84
85	3.081880	.263187	324.4773	895.7819	1.116343	85
86	2.818693	.255302	354.7744	904.6818	1.105361	86
87	2.563391	.241788	390.1083	913.3152	1.094912	87
88	2.321603	.227862	430.7369	921.4917	1.085197	88
89	2.093741	.219957	477.6140	929.1972	1.076198	89
90	1.873784	.215779	533.6795	936.6354	1.067651	90
91	1.658005	.201347	603.1346	943.9323	1.059398	91
92	1.456658	.164375	686.5031	950.7409	1.051811	92
93	1.292283	.154257	773.8241	956.2992	1.045697	93
94	1.138026	.138026	878.7144	961.5157	1.040024	94
95	1.000000	1.000000	1000.000	966.1836	1.035000	95

$*- \Delta a_x = a_x - a_{x+1}.$

161

Table V — Annual Premiums and Differences between First Year and Renewal Premiums

American Experience

x	$1000P_x$	$1000_{19}P_x$	$1000_{20}P_x$	$1000(P_{x+1} -c_x)$	$1000(_{19}P_{x+1} -c_x)$	x
20	13.47758	21.41214	20.72267	6.23156	14.21567	20
21	13.77229	21.75640	21.05670	6.49169	14.52391	21
22	14.08122	22.11345	21.40322	6.76628	14.84496	22
23	14.40531	22.28399	21.76292	7.05635	15.17954	23
24	14.74558	22.86877	22.13654	7.36299	15.52846	24
25	15.10314	23.26861	22.52489	7.68741	15.89260	25
26	15.47921	23.68440	22.92886	8.01938	16.26110	26
27	15.87453	24.11625	23.34859	8.37095	16.64562	27
28	16.29049	24.56516	23.78510	8.74361	17.04727	28
29	16.72860	25.03226	24.23949	9.12720	17.45515	29
30	17.18994	25.51789	24.71217	9.53435	17.88146	30
31	17.67625	26.02336	25.20448	9.96698	18.32765	31
32	18.18948	26.55015	25.71792	10.41504	18.78297	32
33	18.73112	27.09905	26.25333	10.87973	19.24784	33
34	19.30282	27.67093	26.81163	11.37477	19.73549	34
35	19.90704	28.26776	27.39482	11.90278	20.24806	35
36	20.54650	28.89178	28.00518	12.44154	20.76229	36
37	21.22286	29.54361	28.64343	13.01735	21.30399	37
38	21.93933	30.22597	29.31233	13.60796	21.84990	38
39	22.69805	30.93999	30.01312	14.24066	22.42684	39
40	23.50285	31.68903	30.74920	14.89336	23.01172	40
41	24.35653	32.47489	31.52252	15.59450	23.63257	41
42	25.26371	33.30178	32.33736	16.32227	24.26670	42
43	26.22803	34.17246	33.19663	17.09301	24.92989	43
44	27.25437	35.09125	34.10476	17.88391	25.59837	44
45	28.34655	36.06101	35.06480	18.72496	26.30169	45
46	29.51055	37.08729	36.08244	19.57965	27.00240	46
47	30.75047	38.17322	37.16109	20.47799	27.73011	47
48	32.07267	39.32479	38.30693	21.39622	28.46043	48
49	33.48245	40.54666	39.52490	22.32189	29.18030	49
50	34.98469	41.84310	40.81962	23.27030	29.90486	50
51	36.58571	43.22027	42.19752	24.24369	30.63640	51
52	38.29252	44.68523	43.66601	25.24433	31.37759	52
53	40.11286	46.24612	45.23347	26.27458	32.13142	53
54	42.05532	47.91216	46.90929	27.32079	32.88488	54
55	44.12820	49.69229	48.70256	28.39873	33.65469	55
56	46.34173	51.59769	50.62455	29.49317	34.42648	56
57	48.70584	53.63915	52.68625	30.61888	35.21617	57
58	51.23258	55.82987	54.90103	31.77507	36.02429	58
59	53.93502	58.18424	57.28363	32.94159	36.83228	59
60	56.82569	60.71638	59.84860	34.12847	37.65234	60

Table VI — Valuation Columns

$3\frac{1}{2}\%$ $u_x = D_x/D_{x+1}$ $k_x = C_x/D_{x+1}$ $c_x = C_x/D_x$ American Experience

x	u_x	$1000k_x$	$1000c_x$	x	u_x	$1000k_x$	$1000c_x$
15	1.0429615	7.69231	7.37545	55	1.0545847	18.92242	17.94300
16	1.0429903	7.72005	7.40185	56	1.0559986	20.28855	19.21267
17	1.0430102	7.74798	7.42842	57	1.0575633	21.80029	20.61370
18	1.0430594	7.78689	7.46544	58	1.0592955	23.47394	22.15996
19	1.0431002	7.82625	7.50287	59	1.0612337	25.34662	23.88410
20	1.0431414	7.86605	7.54073	60	1.0633853	27.42545	25.79070
21	1.0431945	7.91736	7.58954	61	1.0657798	29.73896	27.90348
22	1.0432483	7.96940	7.63903	62	1.0684330	32.30247	30.23350
23	1.0433030	8.02219	7.68923	63	1.0713654	35.13566	32.79522
24	1.0433584	8.07575	7.74015	64	1.0746245	38.28459	35.62602
25	1.0434146	8.13008	7.79180	65	1.0782698	41.80655	38.77188
26	1.0434836	8.19672	7.85515	66	1.0823041	45.70444	42.22884
27	1.0435537	8.26446	7.91954	67	1.0867824	50.03130	46.03617
28	1.0436250	8.33333	7.98499	68	1.0917744	54.85449	50.24343
29	1.0437097	8.41516	8.06274	69	1.0972840	60.17786	54.84256
30	1.0437959	8.49848	8.14190	70	1.1034030	66.08989	59.89642
31	1.0438837	8.58333	8.22250	71	1.1101166	72.57634	65.37722
32	1.0439858	8.68187	8.31608	72	1.1173879	79.60183	71.23921
33	1.0441024	8.79456	8.42309	73	1.1252177	87.16682	77.46663
34	1.0442214	8.90958	8.53227	74	1.1336596	95.32340	84.08467
35	1.0443430	9.02701	8.64372	75	1.1428516	104.20437	91.17926
36	1.0444930	9.17203	8.78132	76	1.1529599	113.97093	98.85073
37	1.0446465	9.32032	8.92198	77	1.1643135	124.94067	107.30843
38	1.0448300	9.49760	9.09009	78	1.1772427	137.43251	116.74102
39	1.0450179	9.67915	9.26219	79	1.1920305	151.72033	127.27889
40	1.0452375	9.89126	9.46317	80	1.2097705	168.86054	139.58063
41	1.0454626	10.10879	9.66921	81	1.2300994	188.50178	153.24109
42	1.0457212	10.35866	9.90576	82	1.2534772	211.08916	168.40286
43	1.0460008	10.62879	10.16136	83	1.2802451	236.95183	185.08318
44	1.0463305	10.94738	10.46264	84	1.3123838	268.00365	204.21132
45	1.0466842	11.28911	10.78560	85	1.3539172	308.13260	227.58601
46	1.0471064	11.69704	11.17082	86	1.4094689	361.80578	256.69653
47	1.0475714	12.14626	11.59468	87	1.4849792	434.76235	292.77337
48	1.0481111	12.66771	12.08623	88	1.5842440	530.67047	334.96764
49	1.0487448	13.28004	12.66280	89	1.7131878	655.25382	382.47636
50	1.0494631	13.97403	13.31541	90	1.8974999	833.33330	439.17436
51	1.0502715	14.75509	14.04883	91	2.2137496	1138.88883	514.46144
52	1.0511765	15.62944	14.86853	92	2.8298737	1734.17746	612.81091
53	1.0521854	16.60427	15.78074	93	3.8935714	2761.90504	709.34972
54	1.0533233	17.70364	16.80741	94	7.2450014	6000.00000	828.15719

Table VII — Single Premium Pure Endowment

$3\frac{1}{2}\%$ $1000_nE_x = 1000\ D_{x+n}/D_x$ American Experience

x	$n = 1$	$n = 2$	$n = 3$	$n = 4$	$n = 5$	$n = 10$	x
20	958.6428	918.9493	880.8539	844.2934	809.2075	653.8503	20
21	958.5940	918.8551	880.7174	844.1178	808.9956	653.4403	21
22	958.5445	918.7595	880.5790	843.9397	808.7714	653.0088	22
23	958.4943	918.6626	880.4387	843.7494	808.5347	652.5476	23
24	958.4434	918.5643	880.2863	843.5467	808.2852	652.0480	24
25	958.3918	918.4541	880.1215	843.3312	808.0132	651.5091	25
26	958.3284	918.3317	879.9441	843.0928	807.7180	650.9299	26
27	958.2640	918.2072	879.7535	842.8405	807.4084	650.3009	27
28	958.1986	918.0700	879.5493	842.5740	807.0743	649.6206	28
29	958.1208	917.9197	879.3313	842.2829	806.7053	648.8713	29
30	958.0417	917.7666	879.0988	841.9661	806.3100	648.0590	30
31	957.9611	917.5998	878.8408	841.6230	805.8876	647.1653	31
32	957.8675	917.4076	878.5566	841.2530	805.4175	646.1879	32
33	957.7605	917.2006	878.2561	840.8444	804.9080	645.1155	33
34	957.6513	916.9893	877.9276	840.4064	804.3475	643.9447	34
35	957.5399	916.7508	877.5703	839.9169	803.7344	642.6467	35
36	957.4023	916.4844	877.1612	839.3744	803.0466	641.2092	36
37	957.2616	916.1888	876.7207	838.7766	802.3018	639.6088	37
38	957.0935	915.8632	876.2250	838.1218	801.4773	637.8230	38
39	956.9214	915.5062	875.6948	837.4076	800.5802	635.8263	39
40	956.7204	915.1168	875.1059	836.6207	799.5759	633.5668	40
41	956.5144	914.6935	874.4673	835.7467	798.4707	631.0157	41
42	956.2778	914.2228	873.7419	834.7712	797.2172	628.1265	42
43	956.0222	913.6904	872.9380	833.6669	795.8092	624.8667	43
44	955.7209	913.0938	872.0163	832.4170	794.2069	621.1938	44
45	955.3980	912.4173	870.9834	831.0029	792.3786	617.0699	45
46	955.0128	911.6446	869.7977	829.3701	790.2804	612.4471	46
47	954.5889	910.7707	868.4388	827.5077	787.8988	607.2899	47
48	954.0973	909.7516	866.8734	825.3803	785.1967	601.5522	48
49	953.5208	908.5796	865.0902	822.9733	782.1562	595.2007	49
50	952.8682	907.2589	863.0890	820.2823	778.7564	588.1962	50
51	952.1347	905.7801	860.8560	817.2761	774.9744	580.4954	51
52	951.3150	904.1325	858.3619	813.9335	770.7714	572.0485	52
53	950.4028	902.2898	855.5878	810.2167	766.1165	562.8092	53
54	949.3762	900.2370	852.4982	806.0967	760.9743	552.7336	54
55	948.2406	897.9562	849.0804	801.5519	755.3020	541.7772	55
56	946.9709	895.4272	845.3044	796.5299	749.0510	529.8766	56
57	945.5699	892.6403	841.1345	790.9969	742.1766	516.9980	57
58	944.0236	889.5530	836.5293	784.8988	734.6261	503.0980	58
59	942.2995	886.1317	831.4397	778.1861	726.3498	488.1315	59
60	940.3929	882.3519	825.8373	770.8270	717.2989	472.0944	60

Table VII (*Continued*) — Single Premium Pure Endowment

$3\frac{1}{2}\%$ $1000_nE_x = 1000\ D_{x+n}/D_x$ American Experience

x	$n = 15$	$n = 20$	$n = 25$	$n = 30$	To Age 60 $n = 60-x$	To Age 65 $n = 65-x$	x
20	527.2060	423.7336	338.8072	268.4636	157.9093	113.2681	20
21	526.5994	422.8839	337.6604	266.8464	164.7217	118.1547	21
22	525.9447	421.9664	336.3989	265.0483	171.8367	123.2583	22
23	525.2408	420.9686	335.0107	263.0493	179.2684	128.5890	23
24	524.4731	419.8828	333.4738	260.8286	187.0312	134.1573	24
25	523.6402	418.6901	331.7611	258.3611	195.1406	139.9741	25
26	522.7271	417.3822	329.8490	255.6245	203.6126	146.0511	26
27	521.7376	415.9382	327.7172	252.5950	212.4664	152.4019	27
28	520.6561	414.3429	325.3407	249.2489	221.7201	159.0396	28
29	519.4736	412.5695	322.6938	245.5617	231.3926	165.9777	29
30	518.1724	410.5887	319.7486	241.5067	241.5067	173.2325	30
31	516.7425	408.3715	316.4774	237.0578	252.0837	180.8194	31
32	515.1521	405.8878	312.8467	232.1875	263.1461	188.7544	32
33	513.3889	403.1112	308.8302	226.8747	274.7208	197.0569	33
34	511.4253	400.0145	304.4007	221.1014	286.8366	205.7476	34
35	509.2194	396.5579	299.5210	214.8460	299.5210	214.8460	35
36	506.7350	392.7067	294.1573	208.0861	312.8026	224.3730	36
37	503.9470	388.4280	288.2822	200.8165	326.7201	234.3560	37
38	500.8165	383.6838	281.8641	193.0306	341.3071	244.8192	38
39	497.3155	378.4443	274.8830	184.7306	356.6079	255.7944	39
40	493.3942	372.6616	267.3098	175.9315	372.6616	267.3098	40
41	489.0211	366.3017	259.1208	166.6573	389.5199	279.4022	41
42	484.1419	359.3188	250.3004	156.9510	407.2285	292.1045	42
43	478.7207	351.6807	240.8435	146.8846	425.8474	305.4599	43
44	472.7125	343.3547	230.7459	136.5437	445.4368	319.5113	44
45	466.0741	334.3144	220.0310	126.0253	466.0741	334.3144	45
46	458.7541	324.5214	208.7206	115.4207	487.8324	349.9216	46
47	450.7163	313.9676	196.8736	104.8239	510.8125	366.4052	47
48	441.9159	302.6397	184.5726	94.31353	535.1125	383.8356	48
49	432.3240	290.5362	171.9246	83.96829	560.8573	402.3023	49
50	421.9125	277.6841	159.0469	73.87505	588.1962	421.9125	50
51	410.6408	264.1095	146.0503	64.08581	617.2903	442.7816	51
52	398.4872	249.8717	133.0423	54.71713	648.3224	465.0409	52
53	385.4317	235.0654	120.1145	45.88624	681.5012	488.8401	53
54	371.4555	219.8085	107.3549	37.71218	717.0657	514.3504	54
55	356.5738	204.2319	94.86284	30.26791	755.3020	541.7772	55
56	340.7978	188.4582	82.69410	23.57609	796.5299	571.3500	56
57	324.1840	172.6093	70.99009	17.66362	841.1345	603.3448	57
58	306.8273	156.7836	59.89459	12.57957	889.5530	638.0753	58
59	288.8514	141.0756	49.55776	8.411254	942.2995	675.9103	59
60	270.3976	125.5959	40.07392	5.210350	1000.000	717.2989	60

Table VIII — Accumulated Pure Endowment

3½% $1/_nE_x = D_x/D_{x+n}$ American Experience

x	$n = 1$	$n = 2$	$n = 3$	$n = 4$	$n = 5$	$n = 10$	x
20	1.043141	1.088199	1.135262	1.184422	1.235777	1.529402	20
21	1.043194	1.088311	1.135438	1.184669	1.236101	1.530362	21
22	1.043248	1.088424	1.135616	1.184919	1.236443	1.531373	22
23	1.043303	1.088539	1.135797	1.185186	1.236805	1.532455	23
24	1.043358	1.088655	1.135994	1.185471	1.237187	1.533630	24
25	1.043415	1.088786	1.136207	1.185774	1.237604	1.534898	25
26	1.043484	1.088931	1.136436	1.186109	1.238056	1.536264	26
27	1.043554	1.089079	1.136682	1.186464	1.238531	1.537750	27
28	1.043625	1.089242	1.136946	1.186839	1.239043	1.539360	28
29	1.043710	1.089420	1.137228	1.187250	1.239610	1.541138	29
30	1.043796	1.089602	1.137529	1.187696	1.240218	1.543069	30
31	1.043884	1.089800	1.137862	1.188180	1.240868	1.545200	31
32	1.043986	1.090028	1.138231	1.188703	1.241592	1.547537	32
33	1.044102	1.090274	1.138620	1.189281	1.242378	1.550110	33
34	1.044221	1.090525	1.139046	1.189901	1.243244	1.552928	34
35	1.044343	1.090809	1.139510	1.190594	1.244192	1.556065	35
36	1.044493	1.091126	1.140041	1.191364	1.245258	1.559554	36
37	1.044647	1.091478	1.140614	1.192213	1.246414	1.563456	37
38	1.044830	1.091866	1.141259	1.193144	1.247696	1.567833	38
39	1.045018	1.092292	1.141950	1.194162	1.249094	1.572756	39
40	1.045237	1.092757	1.142719	1.195285	1.250663	1.578366	40
41	1.045463	1.093262	1.143553	1.196535	1.252394	1.584747	41
42	1.045721	1.093825	1.144503	1.197933	1.254363	1.592036	42
43	1.046001	1.094463	1.145557	1.199520	1.256583	1.600341	43
44	1.046331	1.095178	1.146768	1.201321	1.259118	1.609803	44
45	1.046684	1.095990	1.148128	1.203365	1.262023	1.620562	45
46	1.047106	1.096919	1.149693	1.205734	1.265374	1.632794	46
47	1.047571	1.097971	1.151492	1.208448	1.269198	1.646660	47
48	1.048111	1.099201	1.153571	1.211563	1.273566	1.662366	48
49	1.048745	1.100619	1.155949	1.215106	1.278517	1.680105	49
50	1.049463	1.102221	1.158629	1.219093	1.284099	1.700113	50
51	1.050272	1.104021	1.161634	1.223577	1.290365	1.722667	51
52	1.051176	1.106033	1.165010	1.228602	1.297402	1.748104	52
53	1.052185	1.108291	1.168787	1.234238	1.305284	1.776801	53
54	1.053323	1.110819	1.173023	1.240546	1.314105	1.809190	54
55	1.054585	1.113640	1.177745	1.247580	1.323974	1.845777	55
56	1.055999	1.116785	1.183006	1.255446	1.335023	1.887232	56
57	1.057563	1.120272	1.188871	1.264228	1.347388	1.934244	57
58	1.059296	1.124160	1.195415	1.274050	1.361237	1.987684	58
59	1.061234	1.128500	1.202733	1.285040	1.376747	2.048628	59
60	1.063385	1.133335	1.210892	1.297308	1.394119	2.118221	60

Table VIII (*Continued*) — Accumulated Pure Endowment

$3\frac{1}{2}\%$ $1/_nE_x = D_x/D_{x+n}$ American Experience

x	$n = 15$	$n = 20$	$n = 25$	$n = 30$	To Age 60 $n=60-x$	To Age 65 $n=65-x$	x
20	1.896792	2.359973	2.951531	3.724900	6.332751	8.828609	20
21	1.898977	2.364715	2.961556	3.747474	6.070846	8.463483	21
22	1.901340	2.369857	2.972661	3.772897	5.819477	8.113044	22
23	1.903889	2.375474	2.984980	3.801569	5.578228	7.776714	23
24	1.906675	2.381617	2.998736	3.833935	5.346700	7.453937	24
25	1.909708	2.388401	3.014217	3.870552	5.124510	7.144176	25
26	1.913044	2.395885	3.031690	3.911988	4.911288	6.846920	26
27	1.916672	2.404204	3.051412	3.958906	4.706627	6.561598	27
28	1.920653	2.413460	3.073701	4.012054	4.510191	6.287743	28
29	1.925026	2.423834	3.098913	4.072297	4.321659	6.024907	29
30	1.929860	2.435527	3.127457	4.140671	4.140671	5.772589	30
31	1.935200	2.448751	3.159783	4.218381	3.966936	5.530381	31
32	1.941174	2.463735	3.196454	4.306864	3.800170	5.297889	32
33	1.947841	2.480705	3.238026	4.407719	3.640059	5.074676	33
34	1.955320	2.499910	3.285143	4.522811	3.486305	4.860324	34
35	1.963790	2.521700	3.338664	4.654496	3.338664	4.654496	35
36	1.973418	2.546430	3.399541	4.805703	3.196904	4.456865	36
37	1.984335	2.574480	3.468824	4.979671	3.060723	4.267013	37
38	1.996739	2.606313	3.547809	5.180527	2.929913	4.084647	38
39	2.010796	2.642397	3.637912	5.413288	2.804201	3.909389	39
40	2.026777	2.683400	3.740978	5.684032	2.683400	3.740978	40
41	2.044902	2.729990	3.859203	6.000338	2.567263	3.579070	41
42	2.065510	2.783044	3.995199	6.371413	2.455624	3.423432	42
43	2.088901	2.843488	4.152075	6.808067	2.348259	3.273752	43
44	2.115451	2.912440	4.333772	7.323663	2.244988	3.129780	44
45	2.145582	2.991196	4.544815	7.934913	2.145582	2.991196	45
46	2.179817	3.081461	4.791094	8.663957	2.049884	2.857783	46
47	2.218690	3.185042	5.079400	9.539809	1.957666	2.729219	47
48	2.262874	3.304259	5.417922	10.60293	1.868766	2.605282	48
49	2.313080	3.441911	5.816504	11.90926	1.782985	2.485693	49
50	2.370160	3.601214	6.287455	13.53637	1.700113	2.370160	50
51	2.435218	3.786308	6.846956	15.60408	1.619983	2.258450	51
52	2.509491	4.002054	7.516404	18.27581	1.542442	2.150348	52
53	2.594493	4.254135	8.325388	21.79303	1.467349	2.045659	53
54	2.692112	4.549414	9.314900	26.51663	1.394572	1.944200	54
55	2.804469	4.896396	10.54154	33.03829	1.323974	1.845777	55
56	2.934292	5.306215	12.09276	42.41585	1.255446	1.750241	56
57	3.084668	5.793429	14.08647	56.61355	1.188871	1.657427	57
58	3.259163	6.378217	16.69600	79.49400	1.124160	1.567213	58
59	3.461987	7.088399	20.17848	118.8883	1.061234	1.479486	59
60	3.698257	7.962042	24.95389	191.9257	1.000000	1.394119	60

Table IX — Temporary Life Annuity Due

$3\frac{1}{2}\%$ $a_{x:\overline{n}|} = (N_x - N_{x+n})/D_x$ American Experience

x	$n = 1$	$n = 2$	$n = 3$	$n = 4$	$n = 5$	$n = 10$	x
20	1.000000	1.958643	2.877592	3.758446	4.602739	8.325336	20
21	1.000000	1.958594	2.877449	3.758166	4.602284	8.323419	21
22	1.000000	1.958545	2.877304	3.757883	4.601823	8.321415	22
23	1.000000	1.958494	2.877157	3.757596	4.601345	8.319305	23
24	1.000000	1.958443	2.877008	3.757294	4.600841	8.317057	24
25	1.000000	1.958392	2.876846	3.756967	4.600299	8.314633	25
26	1.000000	1.958328	2.876660	3.756604	4.599697	8.311989	26
27	1.000000	1.958264	2.876471	3.756225	4.599065	8.309175	27
28	1.000000	1.958199	2.876269	3.755818	4.598392	8.306141	28
29	1.000000	1.958121	2.876041	3.755372	4.597655	8.302832	29
30	1.000000	1.958042	2.875808	3.754907	4.596873	8.299269	30
31	1.000000	1.957961	2.875561	3.754402	4.596025	8.295389	31
32	1.000000	1.957867	2.875275	3.753832	4.595085	8.291103	32
33	1.000000	1.957760	2.874961	3.753217	4.594062	8.286419	33
34	1.000000	1.957651	2.874641	3.752568	4.592975	8.281334	34
35	1.000000	1.957540	2.874291	3.751861	4.591778	8.275746	35
36	1.000000	1.957402	2.873887	3.751048	4.590422	8.269517	36
37	1.000000	1.957262	2.873450	3.750171	4.588948	8.262699	37
38	1.000000	1.957093	2.872957	3.749182	4.587304	8.255118	38
39	1.000000	1.956921	2.872428	3.748122	4.585530	8.246782	39
40	1.000000	1.956720	2.871837	3.746943	4.583564	8.237467	40
41	1.000000	1.956514	2.871208	3.745675	4.581422	8.227099	41
42	1.000000	1.956278	2.870501	3.744243	4.579014	8.215365	42
43	1.000000	1.956022	2.869713	3.742651	4.576318	8.202106	43
44	1.000000	1.955721	2.868815	3.740831	4.573248	8.187020	44
45	1.000000	1.955398	2.867815	3.738799	4.569802	8.169972	45
46	1.000000	1.955013	2.866657	3.736455	4.565825	8.150574	46
47	1.000000	1.954589	2.865360	3.733798	4.561306	8.128710	47
48	1.000000	1.954097	2.863849	3.730722	4.556103	8.104012	48
49	1.000000	1.953521	2.862100	3.727191	4.550164	8.076287	49
50	1.000000	1.952868	2.860127	3.723216	4.543498	8.045433	50
51	1.000000	1.952135	2.857915	3.718771	4.536047	8.011212	51
52	1.000000	1.951315	2.855448	3.713809	4.527743	7.973354	52
53	1.000000	1.950403	2.852693	3.708280	4.518497	7.931550	53
54	1.000000	1.949376	2.849613	3.702111	4.508208	7.885455	54
55	1.000000	1.948241	2.846197	3.695277	4.496829	7.834817	55
56	1.000000	1.946971	2.842398	3.687702	4.484232	7.779244	56
57	1.000000	1.945570	2.838210	3.679345	4.470342	7.718421	57
58	1.000000	1.944024	2.833577	3.670106	4.455005	7.651914	58
59	1.000000	1.942299	2.828431	3.659871	4.438057	7.579272	59
60	1.000000	1.940393	2.822745	3.648582	4.419409	7.500167	60

Table IX (*Continued*) — Temporary Life Annuity Due

$3\frac{1}{2}\%$ $\qquad a_{x:\overline{n}|} = (N_x - N_{x+n})/D_x$ $\qquad$ American Experience

x	$n=15$	$n=20$	$n=25$	$n=30$	To Age 60 $n=60-x$	To Age 65 $n=65-x$	x
20	11.33100	13.75182	15.69403	17.24231	19.40221	20.10008	20
21	11.32665	13.74396	15.68137	17.22307	19.19611	19.92408	21
22	11.32205	13.73558	15.66777	17.20219	18.98208	19.74150	22
23	11.31715	13.72659	15.65307	17.17942	18.75978	19.55204	23
24	11.31190	13.71688	15.63711	17.15447	18.52883	19.35539	24
25	11.30622	13.70636	15.61969	17.12704	18.28885	19.15125	25
26	11.30003	13.69487	15.60056	17.09677	18.03944	18.93928	26
27	11.29337	13.68242	15.57964	17.06346	17.78037	18.71935	27
28	11.28615	13.66884	15.55662	17.02668	17.51122	18.49109	28
29	11.27825	13.65393	15.53119	16.98596	17.23152	18.25414	29
30	11.26969	13.63763	15.50314	16.94100	16.94100	18.00832	30
31	11.26033	13.61968	15.47207	16.89123	16.63915	17.75321	31
32	11.25001	13.59977	15.43753	16.83606	16.32545	17.48840	32
33	11.23867	13.57772	15.39918	16.77502	15.99955	17.21366	33
34	11.22625	13.55332	15.35667	16.70762	15.66107	16.92872	34
35	11.21251	13.52615	15.30940	16.63311	15.30940	16.63311	35
36	11.19717	13.49574	15.25673	16.55070	14.94393	16.32633	36
37	11.18015	13.46189	15.19830	16.45994	14.56433	16.00824	37
38	11.16111	13.42404	15.13336	16.35996	14.16993	15.67831	38
39	11.13990	13.38190	15.06146	16.25023	13.76034	15.33634	39
40	11.11608	13.33479	14.98173	16.12981	13.33479	14.98173	40
41	11.08942	13.28230	14.89363	15.99814	12.89278	14.61423	41
42	11.05936	13.22364	14.79617	15.85422	12.43346	14.23317	42
43	11.02556	13.15827	14.68869	15.69750	11.95621	13.83820	43
44	10.98749	13.08542	14.57031	15.52724	11.46020	13.42877	44
45	10.94483	13.00460	14.44046	15.34317	10.94483	13.00460	45
46	10.89693	12.91495	14.29822	15.14467	10.40910	12.56503	46
47	10.84350	12.81603	14.14321	14.93184	9.852326	12 10982	47
48	10.78393	12.70704	13.97469	14.70440	9.273443	11.63832	48
49	10.71782	12.58748	13.79237	14.46259	8.671487	11.15015	49
50	10.64491	12.45700	13.59623	14.20688	8.045433	10.64491	50
51	10.56476	12.31512	13.38620	13.93767	7.393922	10.12198	51
52	10.47688	12.16134	13.16226	13.65537	6.715354	9.580556	52
53	10.38076	11.99519	12.92454	13.36054	6.007846	9.019679	53
54	10.27584	11.81631	12.67321	13.05386	5.269182	8.438189	54
55	10.16172	11.62461	12.40874	12.73634	4.496829	7.834817	55
56	10.03785	11.41993	12.13152	12.40888	3.687702	7.207894	56
57	9.903836	11.20244	11.84220	12.07266	2.838210	6.555528	57
58	9.759216	10.97227	11.54139	11.72872	1.944024	5.875322	58
59	9.603619	10.72966	11.22989	11.37821	1.000000	5.164407	59
60	9.436989	10.47516	10.90890	11.02264	0.000000	4.419409	60

169

Table X — Foreborne Life Annuity Due

$$_nu_x = (N_x - N_{x+n})/D_{x+n}$$

American Experience

x	$n = 1$	$n = 2$	$n = 3$	$n = 4$	$n = 5$	$n = 10$	x
20	1.043141	2.131394	3.266821	4.451587	5.687960	12.73278	20
21	1.043194	2.131559	3.267165	4.452182	5.688887	12.73784	21
22	1.043248	2.131727	3.267514	4.452786	5.689893	12.74319	22
23	1.043303	2.131897	3.267867	4.453450	5.690968	12.74896	23
24	1.043358	2.132070	3.268264	4.454163	5.692100	12.75528	24
25	1.043415	2.132270	3.268692	4.454913	5.693346	12.76211	25
26	1.043484	2.132485	3.269140	4.455742	5.694682	12.76941	26
27	1.043554	2.132704	3.269633	4.456626	5.696083	12.77743	27
28	1.043625	2.132951	3.270162	4.457552	5.697607	12.78614	28
29	1.043710	2.133216	3.270713	4.458564	5.699299	12.79581	29
30	1.043796	2.133485	3.271314	4.459689	5.701124	12.80635	30
31	1.043884	2.133785	3.271993	4.460906	5.703059	12.81804	31
32	1.043986	2.134130	3.272726	4.462191	5.705221	12.83079	32
33	1.044102	2.134495	3.273488	4.463629	5.707561	12.84486	33
34	1.044221	2.134868	3.274348	4.465183	5.710187	12.86032	34
35	1.044343	2.135302	3.275282	4.466943	5.713054	12.87760	35
36	1.044493	2.135773	3.276349	4.468862	5.716259	12.89675	36
37	1.044647	2.136308	3.277498	4.471001	5.719727	12.91836	37
38	1.044830	2.136884	3.278789	4.473314	5.723560	12.94265	38
39	1.045018	2.137529	3.280170	4.475864	5.727758	12.97018	39
40	1.045237	2.138219	3.281702	4.478664	5.732494	13.00173	40
41	1.045463	2.138984	3.283379	4.481831	5.737746	13.03787	41
42	1.045721	2.139826	3.285296	4.485352	5.743747	13.07916	42
43	1.046001	2.140793	3.287419	4.489384	5.750521	13.12617	43
44	1.046331	2.141862	3.289864	4.493939	5.758258	13.17949	44
45	1.046684	2.143096	3.292618	4.499140	5.767195	13.23995	45
46	1.047106	2.144490	3.295775	4.505172	5.777475	13.30821	46
47	1.047571	2.146082	3.299438	4.512101	5.789203	13.38522	47
48	1.048111	2.147946	3.303653	4.520004	5.802499	13.47184	48
49	1.048745	2.150082	3.308442	4.528932	5.817462	13.56901	49
50	1.049463	2.152493	3.313826	4.538945	5.834300	13.67814	50
51	1.050272	2.155197	3.319853	4.550201	5.853157	13.80065	51
52	1.051176	2.158218	3.326624	4.562792	5.874301	13.93825	52
53	1.052185	2.161615	3.334190	4.576899	5.897924	14.09279	53
54	1.053323	2.165403	3.342662	4.592640	5.924258	14.26629	54
55	1.054585	2.169639	3.352094	4.610153	5.953684	14.46133	55
56	1.055999	2.174349	3.362573	4.629710	5.986551	14.68124	56
57	1.057563	2.179568	3.374264	4.651529	6.023285	14.92931	57
58	1.059296	2.185394	3.387301	4.675897	6.064316	15.20959	58
59	1.061234	2.191886	3.401847	4.703079	6.110082	15.52711	59
60	1.063385	2.199114	3.418040	4.733335	6.161182	15.88701	60

Table X (*Continued*) — Foreborne Life Annuity Due

3½% $_nu_x = (N_x - N_{x+n})/D_{x+n}$ American Experience

x	$n = 15$	$n = 20$	$n = 25$	$n = 30$	To Age 60 $n = 60 - x$	To Age 65 $n = 65 - x$	x
20	21.49255	32.45392	46.32141	64.22588	122.8694	177.4557	20
21	21.50904	32.50055	46.44125	64.54301	116.5366	168.6271	21
22	21.52706	32.55136	46.57497	64.90209	110.4658	160.1636	22
23	21.54659	32.60715	46.72410	65.30874	104.6463	152.0506	23
24	21.56812	32.66836	46.89157	65.76914	99.06808	144.2739	24
25	21.59157	32.73628	47.08113	66.29111	93.72138	136.8199	25
26	21.61746	32.81133	47.29606	66.88235	88.59687	129.6758	26
27	21.64569	32.89531	47.53988	67.55262	83.68558	122.8288	27
28	21.67678	32.98918	47.81641	68.31194	78.97896	116.2672	28
29	21.71092	33.09487	48.12981	69.17188	74.46876	109.9795	29
30	21.74892	33.21483	48.48542	70.14711	70.14711	103.9546	30
31	21.79098	33.35121	48.88839	71.25366	66.00643	98.18201	31
32	21.83822	33.50624	49.34535	72.51063	62.03950	92.65163	32
33	21.89115	33.68233	49.86294	73.93959	58.23933	87.35374	33
34	21.95091	33.88208	50.44886	75.56540	54.59927	82.27906	34
35	22.01902	34.10889	51.11296	77.41874	51.11296	77.41874	35
36	22.09669	34.36596	51.86588	79.53775	47.77430	72.76424	36
37	22.18517	34.65737	52.72022	81.96511	44.57740	68.30738	37
38	22.28582	34.98726	53.69025	84.75320	41.51667	64.04037	38
39	22.40006	35.36028	54.79225	87.96718	38.58676	59.95572	39
40	22.52981	35.78256	56.04633	91.68236	35.78256	56.04633	40
41	22.67677	36.26055	57.47755	95.99422	33.09916	52.30535	41
42	22.84322	36.80197	59.11366	101.0138	30.53190	48.72628	42
43	23.03131	37.41538	60.98855	106.8697	28.07627	45.30285	43
44	23.24349	38.11049	63.14439	113.7163	25.72801	42.02910	44
45	23.48303	38.89932	65.62924	121.7467	23.48303	38.89932	45
46	23.75331	39.79691	68.50414	131.2128	21.33744	35.90812	46
47	24.05837	40.81959	71.83902	142.4469	19.28756	33.05034	47
48	24.40267	41.98734	75.71378	155.9098	17.32989	30.32112	48
49	24.79118	43.32497	80.22336	172.2387	15.46113	27.71584	49
50	25.23014	44.86033	85.48571	192.3096	13.67814	25.23014	50
51	25.72750	46.62884	91.65470	217.4844	11.97803	22.85998	51
52	26.29164	48.67032	98.93289	249.5630	10.35805	20.60153	52
53	26.93280	51.02917	107.6018	291.1667	8.815605	18.45119	53
54	27.66371	53.75731	118.0496	346.1446	7.348256	16.40553	54
55	28.49822	56.91867	130.8072	420.7869	5.953684	14.46133	55
56	29.45397	60.59659	146.7036	526.3334	4.629710	12.61555	56
57	30.55005	64.90054	166.8148	683.4763	3.374264	10.86531	57
58	31.80687	69.98353	192.6949	932.3630	2.185394	9.207882	58
59	33.24761	76.05613	226.6020	1352.737	1.061224	7.640669	59
60	34.90042	83.40367	272.2193	2115.527	1.000000	6.161182	60

Table XI — Single Premium Temporary Insurance

$$3\tfrac{1}{2}\% \qquad 1000 \cdot A^{\,1}_{x:\overline{n}|} = 1000(M_x - M_{x+n})/D_x \qquad \text{American Experience}$$

x	$n = 1$	$n = 2$	$n = 3$	$n = 4$	$n = 5$	$n = 10$	x
20	7.540731	14.81638	21.83627	28.60935	35.14431	64.61659	20
21	7.589535	14.91226	21.97755	28.79443	35.37163	65.09144	21
22	7.639029	15.00950	22.12083	28.98213	35.61140	65.59066	22
23	7.689228	15.10812	22.26615	29.18213	35.86424	66.12328	23
24	7.740148	15.20815	22.42361	29.39507	36.13078	66.69890	24
25	7.791803	15.32012	22.59385	29.62161	36.42117	67.31978	25
26	7.855151	15.44467	22.77754	29.87230	36.73668	67.98831	26
27	7.919537	15.57126	22.97453	30.13740	37.06766	68.71254	27
28	7.984988	15.71070	23.18553	30.41763	37.42454	69.49544	28
29	8.062744	15.86367	23.41126	30.72385	37.81847	70.35657	29
30	8.141901	16.01940	23.65162	31.05634	38.24023	71.28933	30
31	8.222499	16.18898	23.91800	31.41651	38.69127	72.31431	31
32	8.316080	16.38428	24.21185	31.80585	39.19316	73.43658	32
33	8.423085	16.59496	24.52299	32.23523	39.73723	74.66741	33
34	8.532275	16.80994	24.86232	32.69518	40.33455	76.01021	34
35	8.643719	17.05218	25.23142	33.20862	40.98809	77.49720	35
36	8.781321	17.32325	25.65418	33.77861	41.72176	79.14533	36
37	8.921984	17.62358	26.10950	34.40605	42.51636	80.97625	37
38	9.090094	17.95488	26.62185	35.09425	43.39648	83.01840	38
39	9.262189	18.31770	27.16992	35.84434	44.35354	85.29698	39
40	9.463171	18.71390	27.77882	36.67109	45.42435	87.87151	40
41	9.669206	19.14421	28.43874	37.58797	46.60200	90.77316	41
42	9.905757	19.62284	29.18803	38.61185	47.93693	94.05922	42
43	10.16136	20.16388	30.01857	39.77001	49.43611	97.76738	43
44	10.46264	20.77066	30.97067	41.08142	51.14220	101.9504	44
45	10.78560	21.45817	32.03736	42.56427	53.08709	106.6509	45
46	11.17082	22.24389	33.26224	44.27631	55.31971	111.9296	46
47	11.59468	23.13206	34.66497	46.22858	57.85410	117.8262	47
48	12.08623	24.16777	36.28148	48.46004	60.73223	124.3991	48
49	12.66280	25.35931	38.12379	50.98641	63.97354	131.6881	49
50	13.31541	26.70209	40.19169	53.81188	67.59870	139.7360	50
51	14.04883	28.20567	42.49956	56.96832	71.63271	148.5941	51
52	14.86853	29.88098	45.07711	60.47870	76.11653	158.3212	52
53	15.78074	31.75455	47.94434	64.38247	81.08403	168.9742	53
54	16.80741	33.84207	51.13802	68.71117	86.57423	180.6085	54
55	17.94300	36.16123	54.67143	73.48701	92.63136	193.2773	55
56	19.21267	38.73324	58.57587	78.76520	99.30826	207.0571	56
57	20.61370	41.56749	62.88740	84.58084	106.6524	221.9926	57
58	22.15995	44.70711	67.64930	90.99138	114.7216	238.1416	58
59	23.88410	48.18666	72.91282	98.05015	123.5709	255.5646	59
60	25.79070	52.03093	78.70751	105.7910	133.2525	274.2768	60

Table XI (*Continued*) — Single Premium Temporary Insurance

$3\frac{1}{2}\%$ $\qquad$ $1000 \cdot A^1_{x:\overline{n}|} = 1000(M_x - M_{x+n})/D_x$ $\qquad$ American Experience

x	$n = 15$	$n = 20$	$n = 25$	$n = 30$	To Age 60 $n=60-x$	To Age 65 $n=65-x$	x
20	89.61998	111.2291	130.4770	148.4633	185.9773	207.0191	20
21	90.37387	112.3445	132.0518	150.7310	186.1345	208.0841	21
22	91.18414	113.5454	133.7732	153.2352	186.2572	209.1548	22
23	92.05371	114.8473	135.6584	156.0043	186.3431	210.2310	23
24	92.99896	116.2612	137.7349	159.0684	186.3901	211.3125	24
25	94.02389	117.8099	140.0369	162.4636	186.3959	212.3989	25
26	95.14625	119.5064	142.5958	166.2238	186.3581	213.4900	26
27	96.36097	121.3715	145.4352	170.3799	186.2649	214.5766	27
28	97.68668	123.4259	148.5899	174.9698	186.1130	215.6578	28
29	99.13631	125.7033	152.0969	180.0338	185.8989	216.7325	29
30	100.7270	128.2353	155.9905	185.6093	185.6093	217.7906	30
31	102.4735	131.0596	160.3123	191.7411	185.2397	218.8305	31
32	104.4128	134.2165	165.1113	198.4771	184.7854	219.8503	32
33	106.5594	137.7387	170.4245	205.8540	184.2314	220.8387	33
34	108.9430	141.6606	176.2916	213.9067	183.5619	221.7836	34
35	111.6134	146.0360	182.7697	222.6816	182.7697	222.6816	35
36	114.6168	150.9156	189.9147	232.2284	181.8473	223.5290	36
37	117.9802	156.3389	197.7657	242.5671	180.7662	224.3024	37
38	121.7548	162.3630	206.3799	253.7341	179.5164	224.9965	38
39	125.9730	169.0277	215.7925	265.7447	178.0665	225.5854	39
40	130.6998	176.4036	226.0617	278.6160	176.4036	226.0617	40
41	135.9745	184.5384	237.2298	292.3430	174.4924	226.3969	41
42	141.8700	193.5049	249.3460	306.9158	172.3165	226.5807	42
43	148.4341	203.3537	262.4374	322.2820	169.8363	226.5816	43
44	155.7298	214.1433	276.5384	338.3805	167.0201	226.3757	44
45	163.8109	225.9164	291.6442	355.1236	163.8109	225.9164	45
46	172.7507	238.7412	307.7646	372.4405	160.1691	225.1740	46
47	182.5952	252.6401	324.8536	390.2347	156.0171	224.0842	47
48	193.4102	267.6537	342.8534	408.4361	151.2928	222.5979	48
49	205.2376	283.8003	361.6668	426.9586	145.9039	220.6396	49
50	218.1146	301.0645	381.1771	445.6990	139.7360	218.1146	50
51	232.0967	319.4371	401.2763	464.5922	132.6737	214.9292	51
52	247.2221	338.8754	421.8570	483.5071	124.5883	210.9789	52
53	263.5282	359.3000	442.8239	502.3079	115.3349	206.1466	53
54	281.0523	380.6060	464.0826	520.8528	104.7494	200.3002	54
55	299.7932	402.6655	485.5180	539.0346	92.63136	193.2773	55
56	319.7581	425.3607	507.0612	556.7998	78.76520	184.9048	56
57	340.9037	448.5642	528.5492	574.0821	62.88740	174.9707	57
58	363.1510	472.1734	549.8170	590.7970	44.70711	163.2423	58
59	386.3885	496.0856	570.6875	606.8183	23.88410	149.4479	59
60	410.4771	520.1716	591.0262	622.0435	0.000000	133.2525	60

173

Table XII — Accumulated Cost of Insurance

$3\frac{1}{2}\%$ $1000_nk_x = 1000(M_x - M_{x+n})/D_{x+n}$ American Experience

x	$n=1$	$n=2$	$n=3$	$n=4$	$n=5$	$n=10$	x
20	7.866049	16.12318	24.78988	33.88556	43.43053	98.82475	20
21	7.917361	16.22918	24.95414	34.11186	43.72290	99.61345	21
22	7.969405	16.33670	25.12078	34.34147	44.03148	100.4438	22
23	8.022195	16.44577	25.28984	34.58626	44.35708	101.3310	23
24	8.075748	16.55643	25.47309	34.84700	44.70053	102.2914	24
25	8.130081	16.68033	25.67128	35.12452	45.07497	103.3290	25
26	8.196721	16.81818	25.88521	35.43181	45.48206	104.4480	26
27	8.264463	16.95833	26.11474	35.75694	45.90943	105.6627	27
28	8.333333	17.11274	26.36070	36.10084	46.37063	106.9785	28
29	8.415164	17.28220	26.62394	36.47688	46.88016	108.4291	29
30	8.498483	17.45476	26.90439	36.88550	47.42622	110.0044	30
31	8.583333	17.64275	27.21540	37.32848	48.01075	111.7401	31
32	8.681869	17.85932	27.55867	37.80771	48.66192	113.6459	32
33	8.794563	18.09306	27.92236	38.33674	49.36866	115.7427	33
34	8.909584	18.33167	28.31933	38.90401	50.14568	118.0384	34
35	9.027007	18.60067	28.75145	39.53798	50.99705	120.5907	35
36	9.172028	18.90185	29.24682	40.24261	51.95434	123.4314	36
37	9.320320	19.23575	29.78086	41.01933	52.99297	126.6028	37
38	9.497603	19.60432	30.38243	41.87249	54.14561	130.1590	38
39	9.679154	20.00828	31.02670	42.80394	55.40174	134.1514	39
40	9.891261	20.44974	31.74338	43.83240	56.81056	138.6934	40
41	10.10879	20.92964	32.52121	44.97532	58.36407	143.8525	41
42	10.35866	21.46396	33.40578	46.25441	60.13033	149.7457	42
43	10.62879	22.06861	34.38798	47.70491	62.12056	156.4612	43
44	10.94738	22.74756	35.51616	49.35197	64.39405	164.1202	44
45	11.28911	23.51794	36.78298	51.22036	66.99713	172.8343	45
46	11.69704	24.39974	38.24135	53.38546	70.00010	182.7580	46
47	12.14626	25.39834	39.91642	55.86484	73.42834	194.0197	47
48	12.66771	26.56524	41.85327	58.71238	77.34652	206.7969	48
49	13.28004	27.91094	44.06916	61.95390	81.79126	221.2499	49
50	13.97403	29.43161	46.56726	65.60166	86.80340	237.5669	50
51	14.75509	31.13965	49.36895	69.70510	92.43235	255.9780	51
52	15.62944	33.04934	52.51528	74.30423	98.75371	276.7618	52
53	16.60427	35.19330	56.03673	79.46326	105.8377	300.2335	53
54	17.70364	37.59240	59.98607	85.23936	113.7676	326.7552	54
55	18.92242	40.27059	64.38900	91.68092	122.6415	356.7467	55
56	20.28855	43.25672	69.29559	98.88543	132.5788	390.7648	56
57	21.80029	46.56689	74.76498	106.9294	143.7022	429.3878	57
58	23.47394	50.25796	80.86902	115.9275	156.1633	473.3503	58
59	25.34662	54.37867	87.69465	125.9983	170.1259	523.5568	59
60	27.42545	58.96845	95.30631	137.2436	185.7699	580.9787	60

174

Table XII (*Continued*) — Accumulated Cost of Insurance

$3\frac{1}{2}\%$ $1000_nk_x = 1000(M_x - M_{x+n})/D_{x+n}$ American Experience

x	$n = 15$	$n = 20$	$n = 25$	$n = 30$	To Age 60 $n = 60 - x$	To Age 65 $n = 65 - x$	x
20	169.9904	262.4978	385.1068	553.0108	1177.748	1827.690	20
21	171.6179	265.6628	391.0786	564.8607	1129.994	1761.116	21
22	173.3721	269.0863	397.6624	578.1408	1083.919	1696.882	22
23	175.2600	272.8168	404.9375	593.0612	1039.464	1634.907	23
24	177.3188	276.8896	413.0307	609.8580	996.5719	1575.110	24
25	179.5582	281.3773	422.1018	628.8237	955.1876	1517.415	25
26	182.0190	286.3236	432.3064	650.2655	915.2584	1461.749	26
27	184.6924	291.8017	443.7826	674.5180	876.6795	1407.966	27
28	187.6223	297.8834	456.7208	701.9883	839.4052	1356.001	28
29	190.8399	304.6840	471.3350	733.1512	803.3914	1305.793	29
30	194.3890	312.3205	487.8537	768.5470	768.5470	1257.216	30
31	198.3067	320.9322	506.5521	808.8372	734.8340	1210.216	31
32	202.6835	330.6740	527.7706	854.8141	702.2159	1164.742	32
33	207.5608	341.6890	551.8390	907.3468	670.6134	1120.685	33
34	213.0183	354.1388	579.1431	967.4595	639.9529	1077.940	34
35	219.1853	368.2590	610.2068	1036.471	610.2068	1036.471	35
36	226.1869	384.2961	645.6227	1116.021	581.3483	996.2386	36
37	234.1124	402.4915	686.0144	1207.904	553.2752	957.1014	37
38	243.1126	423.1688	732.1963	1314.476	525.9675	919.0312	38
39	253.3061	446.6384	785.0340	1438.553	499.3343	881.9014	39
40	264.8993	473.3613	845.6919	1583.662	473.3613	845.6919	40
41	278.0545	503.7879	915.5181	1754.157	447.9678	810.2903	41
42	293.0340	538.5327	996.1868	1955.487	423.1444	775.6836	42
43	310.0640	578.2339	1089.660	2194.117	398.8196	741.7719	43
44	329.4387	623.6797	1198.454	2478.185	374.9581	708.5061	44
45	351.4696	675.7603	1325.469	2817.875	351.4696	675.7603	45
46	376.5649	735.6715	1474.529	3226.809	328.3282	643.4985	46
47	405.1221	804.6692	1650.061	3722.765	305.4293	611.5747	47
48	437.6629	884.3973	1857.553	4330.620	282.7308	579.9303	48
49	474.7311	976.8156	2103.636	5084.760	260.1445	548.4423	49
50	516.9664	1084.198	2396.634	6033.146	237.5669	516.9664	50
51	565.2060	1209.487	2747.521	7249.532	214.9292	485.4068	51
52	620.4015	1356.197	3170.848	8836.485	192.1704	453.6782	52
53	683.7222	1528.511	3686.680	10946.81	169.2365	421.7057	53
54	756.6244	1731.534	4322.883	13811.26	146.0807	389.4237	54
55	840.7605	1971.610	5118.105	17808.78	122.6415	356.7467	55
56	938.2636	2257.055	6131.770	23617.14	98.88543	323.6279	56
57	1051.575	2598.725	7445.394	32500.82	74.76498	290.0012	57
58	1183.568	3011.624	9179.743	46964.81	50.25796	255.8355	58
59	1337.672	3516.453	11515.61	72143.61	25.34662	221.1061	59
60	1518.050	4141.628	14748.40	119386.1	0.000000	185.7699	60

ANSWERS TO EXERCISES

CHAPTER I

EXERCISES—LIST I. Page 5

2. 1/4; 5/12; 2/3.   **3.** 1/36; 1/36; 1/18.

4. 0.72; 0.18; 0.1.   **5.** 1/221; 1/221; 4/663; 4/663; 8/663.

6. 1/8; 3/8.   **7.** 1/5525; 2/5525; 16/5525.

8. (5) 1/169; 1/169; 1/169; 1/169; 2/169; (7) $(1/13)^3$; $(1/13)^3$; $6(1/13)^3$.

9. 81/256.   **10.** 81/125.   **11.** (a) 3/7; (b) 1/840;

(c) 4/7; (d) 839/840.

12. 1/6; 1/36; 1/18; 5/18.   **13.** 26/49.

14. $1/2^n$; $n/2^n$.   **15.** 5/12.   **16.** 0.224.

EXERCISES—LIST III. Page 14

2. $l_{19} = 97,779$; $d_{19} = 684$; $p_{19} = 0.9930$.

EXERCISES—LIST IV. Page 16

1. (a) 0.8007; (b) 0.0097; (c) 0.2365; (d) 0.0851; (e) 0.0589; (f) 0.0472.

5. 0.5733.

EXERCISES—LIST VI. Page 18

1. $d_{90} = 400$; $q_{90} = 0.4706$; $p_{90} = 0.5294$; $e_{90} = 0.89$; $\overset{\circ}{e}_{90} = 1.39$; etc.

3. (a) 0.99055; (b) 0.00336; (c) 0.99408.

4. 0.7 or 0.8.   **5.** 0.6265; 0.1184.

6. 0.1261; 0.5525; 0.0970.   **8.** 73–74; 0.0306.

CHAPTER II

EXERCISES—LIST VII. Page 24

2. $1161.75; $838.89.

3. (a) $3979.58; $22,225.65; (b) $708.92; $32.06.   **4.** $14,033.97.

EXERCISES—LIST VIII. Page 27

2. $2636.03.   **3.** (c) 0.677233.

4. (a) v^n; (b) $_np_x$; (c) 1.   **5.** $2388.40.

8. $11,545.18.   **9.** (a) $258.36; (b) $236.05.

10. (a) 0.2660398; (b) 17.89939.

EXERCISES—LIST IX.   Page 31

1. \$11,163.24; \$11,763.24; \$8120.79; \$8720.79.
2. \$996.77.   **3.** \$4109.65.
4. \$980.27.   **10.** $l_{21} = 95{,}530$; $l_{20} = 96{,}064$.

EXERCISES—LIST X.   Page 35

1. (b) (1) 11.30613; (2) 10.75900; (3) 11.23968.
5. (a) \$982.76; (b) \$933.62.   **6.** \$1355.33.
7. \$1057.22; \$1056.24.   **8.** \$662.39.
9. $q_{90} = 0.167$; $p_{90} = 0.833$; $a_{90} = 1.972$; $e_{90} = 2.500$; $\overset{\circ}{e}_{90} = 3.000$.

EXERCISES—LIST XI.   Page 38

2. (b) 25.57957.   **4.** \$880.28.

5. \$499.10.   **6.** $\dfrac{10000 D_{25}}{N_{18} - N_{22}}$.

7. \$41,987.60.

8. $50 \dfrac{N_{30} + N_{40}}{D_{30}}$.   **9.** \$437.60.

10. \$9868.30.

EXERCISES—LIST XII.   Page 41

4. \$49.10.   **5.** (a) $\dfrac{10 N_{24} + S_{25} - S_{40}}{D_{24}}$; (b) $\dfrac{100 N_{30} - 5 S_{31} + 5 S_{51}}{D_{30}}$.

EXERCISES—LIST XIII.   Page 45

1. (a) \$20,191.72; (b) \$19,691.72.   **2.** \$1844.37.
3. \$8.69; \$25.88.   **4.** \$25.32.

EXERCISES—LIST XIV.   Page 46

3. \$7047.29.   **4.** $\dfrac{N_{30}^{4\%} - N_{40}^{4\%} + \dfrac{D_{40}^{4\%}}{D_{40}^{5\%}} \cdot N_{40}^{5\%}}{D_{30}^{4\%}}$.

5. (a) \$2232.65; (b) \$2262.65;   **7.** 1.
(c) \$2277.65; (d) \$2287.65.
10. (b) \$59.20; (c) \$56.71.

CHAPTER III

EXERCISES—LIST XV.   Page 52

2. (a) \$1139.90; (b) \$1640.14; (c) \$3583.13.   **3.** \$4877.64.

EXERCISES—LIST XVII. Page 55

1. (a) $73.31; (b) $40.61; (c) $19.89.
3. $299.24; $103.61; $96.16.

EXERCISES—LIST XVIII. Page 58

3. (a) $8.59; (b) $15.45; (c) $15.98.

EXERCISES—LIST XIX. Page 61

2. $38.90; $41.18; $61.65.
3. (a) $87.02; (b) $52.87; (c) $32.35.   **4.** $1319.91.

EXERCISES—LIST XX. Page 64

2. $36.68.   **3.** $67.99.   **4.** $41.47.

EXERCISES—LIST XXI. Page 66

4. (a) $127.29; (b) $27.85.   **6.** (b) $94.48.

EXERCISES—LIST XXII. Page 69

2. $\dfrac{M_x}{N_x - N_{x+20} - R_x + R_{x+20} + 20M_{x+20}}$.

3. (a) $\dfrac{M_x}{D_x - M_x}$; (b) 0.58868.   **4.** $187.36.

EXERCISES—LIST XXIII. Page 70

1. $0.08.   **3.** $\dfrac{1000a_{\overline{10|}} \cdot M_x}{D_x}$.

5. $\dfrac{1000D_{x+n}}{D_x - M_x + M_{x+n}}$.   **8.** (a) $v - \dfrac{a_{x:\overline{20|}}}{a_{x:\overline{20|}}}$; (b) $\dfrac{a_{x:\overline{21|}}}{a_{x:\overline{20|}}} - 1$.

10. $1454.96.   **11.** 1.

13. $a_x = 26(1 - .01x)$; $P_x = \dfrac{x}{26(100 - x)}$.

CHAPTER IV

EXERCISES—LIST XXIV. Page 75

1. Premium 0.186278; Reserves 0.18152, 0.37153, etc.
2. Premium 0.00763552; Reserves 0.00010, 0.00015, etc.

EXERCISES—LIST XXV. Page 77

2. (a) 0; (b) A_{x+n}; (c) 1.

4. (a) \$40.91; (b) \$83.17; (c) \$177.78; (d) \$1.02.

5. (a) \$89.42; (b) \$184.14; (c) \$396.21; (d) \$370.55.

6. (a) \$566.15; (b) \$847.93; (c) \$503.08.

EXERCISES—LIST XXVI. Page 80

2. (a) \$40.91; (b) \$83.17; (c) \$177.78; (d) \$1.02.

4. \$295.96.

3. $\dfrac{M_{x+25} - M_{x+30} + D_{x+30}}{D_{x+25}}$.

5. (a) \$146.54; (b) \$410.03; (c) \$845.00; (d) \$350.96.

EXERCISES—LIST XXVII. Page 81

3. (a) \$46.75216; (b) and (c) \$540.86.

4. (a) and (b) \$358.31.

EXERCISES—LIST XXVIII. Page 84

2. $\dfrac{tV_x}{1 - tV_x}$; $2(tV_x)$.

3. $\dfrac{tV_x}{1 - tV_x}$; $1/2$; $1/3$.

EXERCISES—LIST XXIX. Page 86

4. 10th T.R. \$72.78.

6. (b) \$179.47.

EXERCISES—LIST XXX. Page 89

3. 0.18734.

5. \$38.35.

EXERCISES—LIST XXXII. Page 96

3. 5th T.R. \$447.13.

4. (a) \$17.7241; \$18.2775; \$18.8648; \$19.4891; \$20.1535; \$20.8617.
(b) \$13.64; \$26.41; \$38.40; \$49.66; \$60.26; \$70.24.

EXERCISES—LIST XXXIII. Page 99

1. 3rd year \$7.24; \$24.24; 344 days.

2. \$258.00; \$356.49; 10 yrs. ext. ins. and \$245.27 P.E.

3. \$590.00; \$697.11; 5 yrs. ext. ins. and \$670.81 P.E.

EXERCISES—LIST XXXIV. Page 101

1. \$9.83; \$16.13; \$22.66; \$29.41; \$36.41.

EXERCISES—LIST XXXV. Page 101

2. \$322.06.   **3.** \$726.02.   **6.** 0.2761.

CHAPTER V

EXERCISES—LIST XXXVI.   Page 110

2. (a) $17.05; (b) $10.30.
3. $\alpha = 18.4665$; $\beta = 58.4665$; 10th T.R. $577.02.

EXERCISES—LIST XXXVII.   Page 113

1. (a) $51.58; (b) $88.87.   **2.** (a) $51.58; (b) $88.87.
3. $P = 87.0186$; $\alpha = 8.6437$; $\beta = 97.7907$;   N.L. $446.14;
F.P.T. $396.77.
6. (a) 8.1419; 128.954; (b) $537.92.

EXERCISES—LIST XXXVIII.   Page 116

2. (a) 74.4947; 89.3881; (b) and (c) $436.98.
3. $368.56; $846.36.   **5.** Premiums 78.2906, 87.8249;
                                      Reserves $73.22, $159.53, etc.
7. $442.88, $544.99, etc.

EXERCISES—LIST XXXIX.   Page 120

2. (a) 30.6975; 23.0101; (b), (c), (f), and (g) $468.57;
(d) and (e) 15.2183.
3. (a) 34.9369; (b), (c), and (d) $240.70.

4.

Policy	α_O	β_O	5th Modified Reserve
10 yr. endowment	$76.56	$88.46	$439.56
10 payt. 15 yr. end.	64.56	76.46	371.00
10 payt. 20 yr. end.	55.10	67.00	316.99
10 payt. end. at 60	47.82	59.72	275.36
10 payt. end. at 65	42.41	54.31	244.45

6. (a) 2.7800; (b) 8.0985; (c) 30.5879.
7. $660.17; $653.80.

EXERCISES—LIST XL.   Page 124

3. (a) $49.20; $67.08; (b) $24.88; $42.76; (c) $13.61; $31.49.
5. $438.35; $541.28; etc.
6. Premiums 72.4723, 88.3649; Reserves $67.49, $154.43, etc.
7. $373.66; $850.55.

EXERCISES—LIST XLI. Page 127

1. (a) 16.7201; 30.9358; 29.9021; (b) \$273.33; (c) \$875.37.
2. (a) 10.1626; 33.1743; (b) \$256.31.

EXERCISES—LIST XLII. Page 131

3. (a) 31.9978; 14.1164; (b) \$467.02; (c) 5.9745.
4. (a) 7.6804; (b) 2.0459.

EXERCISES—LIST XLIII. Page 135

1. 13.3154; 38.6019; 36.5720; 5th T.R. \$105.94.
2. Group (c); 7.5407; 18.5227; 17.7241; 10th T.R. \$120.22.
3. 9.4632; 24.6411; 23.5028; 5th T.R. \$65.46.

EXERCISES—LIST XLIV. Page 138

1.

Policy	α_I	β_I	5th Modified Reserve
10 yr. endowment	\$70.95	\$88.83	\$436.83
10 payt. 15 yr. end.	58.85	76.73	367.83
10 payt. 20 yr. end.	49.20	67.08	312.82

2.

Policy	α_I	β_I	10th Modified Reserve
20 yr. endowment	\$22.94	\$40.82	\$385.18
30 yr. endowment	8.64	26.52	202.07
25 yr. endowment	14.12	32.00	272.18
20 payt. 30 yr. end.	14.75	32.63	280.28

6. N.L. \$86.68; F.P.T. \$8.14; \$97.44; O.L. Mod. \$78.29, \$87.83;
20 P.L. Mod. \$70.95, \$88.83.
9. (a) \$177,929.17; (b) \$170,432.80; (c) \$1,491,948; (d) \$61,751.
10. Ten years.   **11.** \$29.418.   **12.** \$39.733.

CHAPTER VI

EXERCISES—LIST XLV.   Page 147

1. $8.19.   **2.** $92.95.
3. (a) $26.91; (b) $22.01.

EXERCISES—LIST XLVI.   Page 150

1. (a) $2.67; $16.60; $30.95; $45.78; $60.94; (b) $5.50.
2. (a) $21.54; $59.13; $98.32; $139.25; $181.88; (b) $6.30.

EXERCISES—LIST XLVII.   Page 151

2. $38.40; $45.37.   **3.** 0.001572; 0.08575.

INDEX TO NOTATION

Number indicates the page upon which the definition of the symbol appears.

185

ALPHABETICAL INDEX

Numbers refer to pages

187